SAHA AND HIS FORMULA

Vignettes in Physics
A Series by G. Venkataraman

Published
The Many Phases of Matter
Why Are Things the Way They Are?
Bose and His Statistics
Chandrasekhar and His Limit
A Hot Story
At the Speed of Light
The Quantum Revolution (3 vols.)
1. The Breakthrough
2. QED: The Jewel of Physics
3. What is Reality?
Raman and His Effect
Bhabha and His Magnificent Obsessions
Saha and His Formula

Forthcoming
The Big and The Small

Vignettes in Physics

SAHA AND
HIS FORMULA

G. Venkataraman

Universities Press

UNIVERSITIES PRESS (INDIA) LIMITED

Registered Office
3-5-820 Hyderguda, Hyderabad 500 029 (A.P.), India

Distributed by
Orient Longman Limited

Registered Office
3-6-272 Himayatnagar, Hyderabad 500 029 (A.P.), India

Other Offices
Bangalore/Bhubaneshwar/Calcutta/Chennai
Ernakulam/Guwahati/Hyderabad/Jaipur
Lucknow/Mumbai/New Delhi/Patna

First Published 1995
Reprinted 1997
ISBN 81 7371 017 1

Frontispiece : Meghnad Saha

Typeset by
Access Center
Secunderabad 500 003

Printed in India by
Navya Printers
Hyderabad 500 482

Published by
Universities Press (India) Limited
3-5-820 Hyderguda, Hyderabad 500 029

The maps in this book are not to scale. The external boundaries of
India as depicted are neither correct nor authentic.

Contents

Preface

To the adult reader

This book and others in this series written by me are inspired by the memory of my son Suresh who left this world soon after completing school. Suresh and I often used to discuss physics. It was then that I introduced him to the celebrated *Feynman Lectures*.

Hans Bethe has described Feynman as the most original scientist of this century. To that perhaps may be added the statement that Feynman was also the most scintillating teacher of physics in this century.

The Feynman Lectures are great but they are at the textbook level and meant for serious reading. Moreover, they are a bit expensive, at least for the average Indian student. It seemed to me that there was scope for small books on diverse topics in physics which would stimulate interest, making at least some of our young students take up later a serious study of physics and reach for the Feynman as well as the Landau classics.

Small books inevitably remind me of Gamow's famous volumes. They were wonderful, and stimulated me to no small extent. Times have changed, physics has grown and we clearly need other books, though written in the same spirit.

In attempting these volumes, I have chosen a style of my own. I have come across many books on popular science where elaborate sentences often tend to obscure the scientific essence. I have therefore opted for simple English, and I don't make any apologies for it. If a simple style was good enough for the great Enrico Fermi, it is also good enough for me. I have also employed at times a chatty style. This is deliberate. Feynman uses this with consummate skill, and I have decided to follow in his footsteps (whether I have succeeded or not, is for readers to say). This book is meant to be read for fun and excitement. It is a book you can even lie down in bed and read, without going to sleep I hope!

Naturally I have some basic objectives, the most important of which is to stimulate the curiosity of the reader. Here and there the reader may fail to grasp some details, and in fact I have deliberately pitched things a bit high on occasions. But if the reader is able to experience at least in some small measure the *excitement* of science, then my purpose would have been achieved. Apart from excitement, I have also tried to convey that although we might draw boundaries and try to compartmentalise Nature into different subjects, she herself knows no such boundaries. So we can always start anywhere, take a random walk and catch a good glimpse of Nature's glory. Where she is concerned, all topics are "fashionable". There is today an unnecessary polarisation of the young towards subjects that are supposed to be fashionable. To my mind this is unhealthy, and I have tried to counter it.

This series is essentially meant for the curious. With humility, I would like to regard it as some sort of a "Junior Feynman Series", if one might call it that. With much love, and sadness, it is dedicated to the memory of Suresh who inspired it.

To the young reader

The Sun is often described as a great big ball of fire. It is in fact a star, and though there are billions and billions of stars in the Universe, the Sun is very special to us because it is *our* star. Recognising it as the source of energy for life on Earth, our ancients worshipped the Sun. In more recent times, worship of the Sun has declined but on the other hand, scientific study of it has greatly increased. The mysteries of the Sun have not been completely unravelled but all the same, we do know quite a bit about it. A great leap forward occurred way back in 1920 when Meghnad Saha made an important discovery which at one stroke not only swept away much of the prevailing confusion but also paved the way for a systematic study of stellar atmospheres in general. This book is about that great discovery and the man who made it.

Acknowledgements

This is the twelfth book in this series. When I first started, little did I dream that I would get this far and if I have been able to do so, it is in no small measure due to the sustained support and encouragement I have received from my wife Saraswati.

This particular volume owes much to Prof. S.K. Joshi who not only took keen interest in its progress but also helped me in various ways at various times, including in obtaining the Collected

Scientific Works of Meghnad Saha. I am also indebted to Prof. S.K. Sahni of INSA for a picture of the 1980 eclipse which forms the theme of the cover. Thanks are also due to Mr. John Vincent and Mrs. Girija Srinivasan for helping with source material. The technical photographs reproduced in this volume are through the courtesy of Prof. G. Srinivasan, while the Saha Institute of Nuclear Physics (SINP) kindly supplied the pictures relating to the life of Saha. I am also grateful to SINP for helping me with biographical material and copies of various articles that Saha wrote. Thanks are due to Dr. Santimay Chatterjee for providing the photograph of Indian research scholars in London, 1921. The Publishers too have been most helpful, and it is a real pleasure to thank them. And then of course there is Mrs. G. Naga Nirmala, who has become more indispensable to this series than the author, for without her there is no typescript.

Writing this series has been an inspiring education for me, and if I have achieved anything at all it is due to the guidance of the Divine Master — He writes, and I merely hold the pen.

G. VENKATARAMAN

1 *The Early Years*

The period 1920–1930 may truly be hailed as the golden era of physics in India, for during that decade were made four important discoveries namely, the Saha ionisation formula, Bose statistics, the Raman effect and the Chandrasekhar limit. This book is about the first of these four discoveries and the man who made it.

Meghnad Saha was born on 6 October 1893 as the fifth child of Jagannath Saha and Bhubaneswari Debi. Jagannath was a shop-keeper in a small village named Seoratali about 40 km from Dacca. Today Dacca is the capital of Bangladesh but in those days it was a part of the Province of Bengal in British India. The Sahas were not rich and barely managed to make both ends meet. Young Meghnad was admitted to the primary school in Seoratali where he did so well that his teachers wanted him to enter an English-medium school. The nearest such school was in another village about 10 km away. Jagannath Saha was not in favour of further education for Meghnad as it was a burden he could not carry. Besides, the eldest son Jayant had already received such education but was none the better for it as he was jobless. So Jagannath wanted young Meghnad to assist him in shopkeeping. However, brother Jayant and the primary school teachers were able to persuade the father to relent and Meghnad went to the neighbouring village to live there and attend an English-medium school. Here he was lucky in that one Mr. Anantha Kumar Das, a medical practitioner, took interest in Meghnad and offered him free boarding and lodging. Later in life, Saha never failed (whenever the occasion arose) to express his gratitude to Anantha Kumar Das for timely help at a crucial stage, but for which his educational career might have been sharply cut off.

In 1905, Meghnad went to Dacca and joined the Government Collegiate School to prepare for entrance to College. Here he not only received a free studentship (i.e., was exempted from paying fees), but also a stipend. This was the period when the British partitioned the province of Bengal, much against the will of the people (see Box 1.1). Naturally there were protests everywhere, and when the British Governor of Bengal Sir Bampfylde Fuller came on a visit to Dacca, a boycott was organised. All the students of the

Collegiate School who participated in the protest were dismissed. Saha was one of them and so suddenly he lost both his stipend as well as free studentship. But he managed to pull through by joining the Kishori Lal Jubilee School where again he received free studentship and a stipend; brother Jayant took care of the living expenses.

Box 1.1 It suffices to describe one incident which greatly aroused public anger during the days of the British rule, and that is the partition of Bengal. Around the turn of the century, the province of Bengal was very large, comprising not only today's West Bengal but parts of Bihar and Bangladesh as well. Around 1905, the British partitioned Bengal into two provinces. The people of Bengal strongly resented this, suspecting that the British wanted to weaken the people of Bengal by dividing them. The popular feeling was that the British were trying to dissipate the Swadeshi movement by this process. Contrary to the result expected by the British, the partition of Bengal infuriated the people even more, and their agitation against the British rulers became violent at times. In a letter to his daughter Indira, Nehru described these events as follows:

> Governments have only one method of meeting an argument or demand which they do not like — the use of the bludgeon. So the Government indulged in repression and sent people to prison, and curbed the newspapers with press laws, and let loose crowds of secret policemen and spies to shadow everybody they did not like ... But repression did not succeed in crushing Bengal... Finally in 1911 the British Government reversed the partition of Bengal. This triumph put new heart in the Bengalis.

Around this time, Saha joined the Bible classes run by the Dacca Baptist Society. In a test that was conducted, Saha stood first and won a handsome prize of Rs.100/- plus a beautifully bound copy of the Bible (in those days, hundred rupees went a long way!). In 1909 Saha passed the Collegiate entrance exam, standing first among the candidates from East Bengal. This got him entry into the Intermediate Dacca College where he spent two years studying Intermediate. During this period, Saha also took private lessons in German which later was to stand him in good stead.

In 1911 Saha came to Calcutta and joined the Presidency College to study for the B.Sc. degree in Applied Mathematics (we would call it mathematical physics). Once again he was dependent on a stipend plus free studentship. S.N. Bose was his classmate and Mahalanobis (see Box 1.2) was one year senior. The great freedom fighter Netaji Subhas Chandra Bose was Saha's junior by one year.

His teachers included J.C. Bose (see Box 1.3) and P.C. Ray (see Box 1.4). After B.Sc. came M.Sc., and once again S.N. Bose was his classmate. Both in B.Sc. and M.Sc., Bose secured the first rank while Saha stood second.

Box 1.2 Prasantha Chandra Mahalanobis was born in a well to do family in Calcutta in the year 1893. After receiving the B.Sc. degree in physics in 1912, he left for England for further studies. As the result of a chance encounter with a friend in Cambridge, he decided to study mathematics. Later, finding mathematics too abstract, he again switched over to physics.

In Cambridge, Mahalanobis came into contact with the mathematics genius Ramanujan. One day Ramanujan invited Mahalanobis for lunch and while he was cooking, Mahalanobis kept himself busy with a small mathematics puzzle. After working out the solution, Mahalanobis read out the problem to Ramanujan. From the kitchen the latter dictated a continued fraction, and said the first term of that was the solution to the problem Mahalanobis was solving!

After completing the Cambridge Tripos examination in physics, Mahalanobis went to the Cavendish Laboratory of which Rutherford was the head. It was decided that Mahalanobis would work under C.T.R. Wilson (famous for his invention of the cloud chamber). Mahalanobis then returned to India on what he thought was a short vacation. Meanwhile, the First World War broke out and Mahalanobis was grounded in India. This was a turning point because thereafter Mahalanobis stayed in the country, in the process making great contributions to it. Decades later, Homi Bhabha was similarly forced to stay back in India consequent upon the outbreak of the Second World War. And like Mahalanobis, Bhabha too made worthy contributions to the nation.

Getting back to Mahalanobis, a physics lecturer's job was vacant in the Presidency College since the Englishman holding the job had gone off to fight in the war. Mahalanobis was appointed to that post. Although he was teaching physics (and planned to pursue physics research under Wilson after the war), Mahalanobis became increasingly interested in mathematical statistics and its applications. This led to the founding of the Indian Statistical Institute which has now grown very big with several branches throughout India. Of course, all this was possible because of the excellent research work done by Mahalanobis himself and for which he received international recognition. A favourite of Nehru, he was invited to join the Planning Commission. The Second Five Year Plan was largely his brain child. Mahalanobis died in 1972.

While in college, Saha flirted a bit with some revolutionaries including one Bagha Jatin (Jatindranath Mukherjee). The prefix Bagha (meaning tiger) was given to Jatin because he had killed a tiger single-handed with a dagger, while engaged in gun running in the jungles of Sunderbans. Although Saha was emotionally

> **Box 1.3** Sir Jagdish Chandra Bose was perhaps the first Indian to establish an international scientific reputation. He was born in 1858 and, after completing college education in Calcutta, went to England to study medicine. But physics attracted him more and he switched over to it. He returned to India after getting the D.Sc. degree in Physics from the London University in 1896. In Calcutta, Bose was appointed Professor of Physics in the Presidency College, a post reserved for Englishmen at that time. Since he was not an Englishman, Bose was given a lower salary but he protested and refused to draw his pay! The authorities then came to their senses.
>
> Bose did pioneering work in millimeter waves. Several years before Marconi, he generated and transmitted electromagnetic waves through walls. Naturally, Bose became famous after this demonstration. Later, he repeated this experiment in London before a distinguished audience which included Lord Kelvin. In 1917, Bose founded the Bose Institute in Calcutta. His interests now switched to plant physiology, and he used his experience in physics to demonstrate through clever experiments that plants not only lived, but also responded to stimuli.

> **Box 1.4** Acharya Prafulla Chandra Ray was born in 1861. After completing college education in Calcutta, he went abroad to study at the University of Edinburgh, where he obtained a doctorate degree in chemistry. On return to India, he too joined the staff of the Presidency College.
>
> Ray became famous for his work on mercurous nitrate which until then defied preparation. Later, he spent many years studying the salts of mercury. Ray was promoted to the Professor's post but he moved over to the University as the Palit Professor of Chemistry in 1916.
>
> Like many others of those days, Ray was swept by the nationalist fervour. He dreamt of big chemical industries in India, and himself founded one, the Bengal Chemicals Ltd., which is still in existence.
>
> Satyen Bose was a student of Ray in college. Apparently, Ray used to make young Satyen sit on a stool by his side during the lectures to prevent him from asking difficult questions!

sympathetic to the cause of freedom, he did not become involved with revolutionary activities. His goal was to get a job, earn money and support his family which was very much looking up to him. After college he tried to appear for the Financial Civil Service (FCS) examination and enter the FCS but he was denied permission to write the exam as he was suspected of contacts with revolutionaries; besides, there was also the boycott he had participated in as a school student. Not being able to join Government service was a big blow to Saha but as it turned out it was a great boon for science. Meanwhile, a living had to be eked out and Saha did this by going up and down Calcutta on a bicycle giving private tuition. It was around this time that Sir Ashutosh Mookerjee became the Vice Chancellor of Calcutta University. (For more about Sir Ashutosh, see the companion volumes *Raman and His Effect* and *Bose and His Statistics.*) Sir Ashutosh Mookerjee offered lecturerships to both Saha and Bose in the Department of Mathematics but because they could not get along with Dr. Ganesh Prasad, the professor, he transferred them to the Physics Department where Raman had been appointed the Palit Professor. See also Box 1.5.

Box 1.5 Satyen Bose has reminisced about the days when Saha, he and others joined the Calcutta University to teach. This is what he said in part:

Meghnad, Sailen and I went up the steep stairs to the library, to the special chamber where Sir Ashutosh sat. We were meek and submissive and overawed by his august presence. He had heard that the younger generation wanted more modern subjects to be introduced in the University curriculum. He asked — "What subjects are you competent to teach, boys?"

"Sir, we will try our best to teach whatever you want us to." He smiled, we had only heard of the many new discoveries in physics, most of them made in Germany — new developments and new discoveries. Planck, Einstein, Bohr — we Bengalis had only heard of them. To know more about them one had to read German books or research journals in other languages. During the war most of these journals did not come to India.

At long last, as the first step to a new career, we were given a special allowance of Rs.125/- per month. Meghnad was to study quantum theory and I had to learn Einstein's relativity theory. We came away committing ourselves to being prepared to teach within a year. But where were we to get the books from? There were some books in English on relativity — we got hold of them. But where could we get hold of Boltzmann, Kirchhoff, Planck? Suddenly, I thought of an idea. Dr. Bruhl was the answer.

Bruhl was then teaching Physics at Sibpur College ... He was fond of reading and had an excellent collection of science books in his library, where we discovered many rare books. We borrowed Planck, Boltzmann, Wien — we could not have asked for more. Meghnad had taken great pains to learn German and even passed the Intermediate Examination. I had just started. But I read French...

But the chemists did not approve of these schemes hatched by the younger generation ... In their opinion, prompted by a few immature youngsters, Ashutosh was being too hasty — he ought to wait for Deben Bose and Raman to come; the youngsters were hardly capable of carrying the heavy burden.

> Ashutosh felt that if he could win over Acharya Ray to his side, he would not have any difficulty in carrying through his plans in the Senate. Not that Dr. Ray had much faith in us, but fortunately our classmate Jnan (J.C. Ghosh) had already earned the Acharya's appreciation by taking the step towards his famous theory. The old man had faith in the capability of the youngsters. So Ashutosh had little problem in winning him over. The new system was introduced from 1917, when postgraduate courses in applied mathematics, physics, chemistry etc., were to commence in Science College as well. Of course, Presidency College would continue with its old syllabus.

Saha and Bose worked closely together in teaching, in learning advanced physics and in research. The knowledge of German picked up earlier came in very handy now for they could read many of the advanced texts and research papers published in German. Both Saha and Bose strongly believed that to be effective as teachers, they must also engage in research. Thus they both began to pick up problems, solve them and publish papers. While they published independently, they also collaborated on one paper. And in the year 1920, that is roughly about four years after he started his career, Saha published a paper that became a turning point in his life. To appreciate why and how that paper made such an impact we need to delve a bit into physics, which we do in the chapters that follow.

2 *A Primer On Atomic Spectra*

To understand the significance of Saha's discovery, it is necessary to have some background about (a) atomic spectra, and (b) the spectra of the light coming from the stars. Presently let us take a brief look at the story of atomic spectra.

The story begins with Newton who discovered that sunlight is split into various colours when it is passed through a prism. The next important landmark is the discovery by Fraunhofer about which you will hear more in the next chapter. Basically, Fraunhofer found that the so-called continuous spectrum of the Sun discovered by Newton is actually riddled with numerous dark lines, now known as *Fraunhofer lines*. He was able to make this discovery because he examined sunlight with a better arrangement than Newton did — see Fig.2.1. In fact, it was Fraunhofer who invented what we now call the spectroscope. Once this instrument became available, scientists began to examine the spectra of light coming from all sorts of luminous objects, particularly flames, gas discharges, arcs and sparks. In all these cases, the spectrum was generally found to consist of a series of lines, some bright and some faint, some sharp and some diffuse. Unlike Fraunhofer lines which are dark, all emission lines are luminous. Meanwhile photography had been invented and one could now record spectra, thereby catching even faint lines.

Study of spectra rapidly became an important activity and soon an impressive amount of data was accumulated. For instance, when sodium is inserted into a flame, the flame becomes bright yellow. When examined with a spectroscope numerous lines are seen, prominent among them being two lines called D_1 and D_2. Next time you see a sodium vapour lamp in the street, pause a second to note that the yellow colour is mostly due to the D_1 and D_2 lines.

Everyone knew that the atoms were in some way connected with spectra but no one knew how. In a sense the situation was like what obtained in astronomy when Tycho Brahe had accumulated a lot of observations. You will recall that later came Kepler who by analysing the voluminous data of Tycho discovered patterns — the Kepler's laws. And finally, Newton explained Kepler's laws.

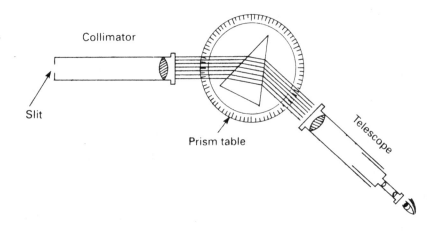

Collimator

Slit

Prism table

Telescope

Fig.2.1 Schematic of the spectroscope invented by Fraunhofer. It is an improvement over Newton's arrangement in that Fraunhofer added a slit, a collimator and a telescope.

Something similar happened in the case of atomic spectra also. To start with, there was the Swiss school teacher Balmer who in 1885 noticed that the four prominent lines of the spectrum of (atomic) hydrogen (see Fig.2.2) could be represented by the following simple formula for the wavelength λ:

$$\lambda = 3645.98 \frac{m^2}{m^2 - 2^2} \tag{2.1}$$

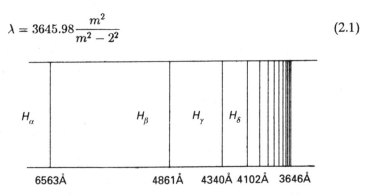

H_α H_β H_γ H_δ

6563Å   4861Å   4340Å 4102Å   3646Å

Fig.2.2 Schematic of the Balmer series in hydrogen as it would appear when a photograph is taken of the spectrum. Balmer recognised only the four lines labelled H_α, H_β, H_γ and H_δ. Later other lines were identified upto the cut-off at 3646 Å. The Balmer series occurs in the visible part of the spectrum. Other series (see Fig.2.3) were discovered later which were outside the visible region (see also equation (2.3)).

Here λ is the wavelength expressed in Ångström ($1\text{Å} = 10^{-8}$ cm) while m takes on the values 3, 4, 5 and 6. Corresponding to these values of m, we get the wavelengths of the four lines H_α, H_β, H_γ and H_δ respectively. In spect roscopy, spectral lines are often characterized in terms of their frequencies, the frequency ν being expressed in units of cm^{-1}. Frequency so expressed is sometimes referred to as the wave number and corresponds to the number of waves of that wavelength which can be accommodated in 1 cm. In these units, Balmer's formula becomes

$$\nu = N\left(\frac{1}{2^2} - \frac{1}{m^2}\right), \ m = 3, \ 4, \ 5 \text{ and } 6 \tag{2.2}$$

with $N = 109678.3$ cm^{-1}. After Balmer's came two related discoveries. Firstly it was realised that the Balmer series did not stop with $m = 6$ and that in fact there were many more lines in the series, converging to the cut-off frequency $(N/4)$, which applies when $m = \infty$. Secondly, other series (in hydrogen) similar to the Balmer series were discovered and all these could be comprehensively described by the formula

$$\nu = N\left(\frac{1}{n^2} - \frac{1}{m^2}\right) \tag{2.3}$$

with

$$
\begin{array}{lll}
n = 1, & m = 2, \ 3, \ 4 & \text{for the Lyman series} \\
n = 2, & m = 3, \ 4, \ 5 & \text{for the Balmer series} \\
n = 3, & m = 5, \ 6, \ 7 & \text{for the Paschen series} \\
n = 4, & m = 5, \ 6, \ 7 & \text{for the Brackett series,}
\end{array}
$$

and so on.

One now had compact formulae (to describe the hydrogen spectrum) but one still did not know why those formulae worked. That mystery was cleared up by Neils Bohr, whose famous model for the atom has been mentioned in many companion volumes (e.g., *Why Are Things the Way They Are?*). Bohr pointed out that an atom can have only specific energy states called stationary states, and that spectral lines are emitted when the atom makes a transition from a state of higher energy to a state of lower energy. The hydrogen atom series can thus be pictured as in Fig.2.3. An atom can not only make a downward transition in energy (in the process emitting a spectral line) but can also make an upward transition, provided the requisite energy is supplied; thus, instead of energy emission there is energy absorption.

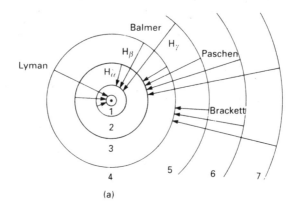

(a)

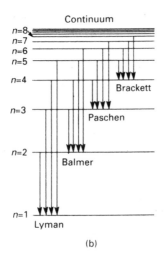

(b)

Fig.2.3 Two view points of the transitions in the hydrogen atom, illustrating the origin of the various series of spectral lines. (a) shows transitions between various orbits while (b) shows transitions between various energy levels.

The Bohr model worked wonderfully well for hydrogen but fared poorly even in the case of the next simplest atom, i.e., helium (see *Why Are Things the Way They Are?*). There were various guesses as to what was going wrong, and all kinds of patch-ups and extensions were tried. A famous extension is that due to Arnold Sommerfeld who argued that if planets can go round in elliptic orbits, then why can't the electron? Now the velocity of the electron in the Bohr orbit is quite high and at such velocities the mass is expected to vary on account of relativistic effects (see *At The Speed of Light*); such relativistic effects could make the orbit elliptic. In this manner, Sommerfeld came up with a new scheme which is illustrated in Fig.2.4. In this, there is only one orbit corresponding to $n = 1$, a circular orbit in fact but for $n = 2$ there are two orbits, one circular and the other elliptical. For $n = 3$ there are three of them, one circular, the next one elliptical and the third one an even more elongated ellipse; and so on. Corresponding to the proliferation of orbits, there is also an increase in the number of energy levels as shown in Fig.2.5. Using this scheme, Sommerfeld was able to explain the so-called fine structure of some spectral lines, i.e., the fact that what seemed like single lines in the older data represented actually a bunch or cluster of lines which could be seen separated only under high resolution.

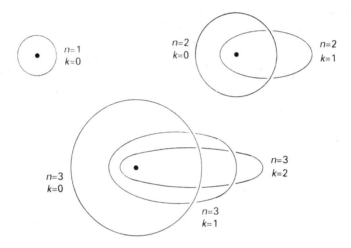

Fig.2.4 Elliptic orbits in the hydrogen atom (according to Sommerfeld's model). Compare with Fig.2.3(a). For each value of n, the principal quantum number, there is a family of n orbits labelled by the *azimuthal* quantum number k. The integer k can take on the values 0, 1, 2, ... , $(n-1)$. For convenience, the different families are shown separately.

Like the Bohr model, the Sommerfeld model also failed when applied to complex atoms (i.e., atoms with many electrons) but nevertheless in many ways it played a useful role. For instance, it showed that energy levels cannot be labelled by just one quantum number, i.e., with the principal quantum number n as Bohr sought to do, but that more were required. Sommerfeld had two quantum numbers, i.e., in addition to Bohr's n, he had another one denoted k and called the *azimuthal* quantum number. For each value of n, k took the integer values 0, 1, ... , $(n-1)$. Thus the family of orbits corresponding to a given n correspond really to different values of k allowed for that particular n.

At this stage, it is necessary to introduce some notation to label the various orbits. One could of course simply label them via the values for the quantum numbers n and k (e.g., $n = 2$, $k = 0, 1$), but historically $k = 0$ was denoted by s, $k = 1$ by p, $k = 2$ by d and $k = 3$ by f. You might wonder why this peculiar notation. It was noticed while studying spectra that there were series or families of spectral lines. Over the years they had been labelled sharp, principal, diffuse, etc. With the advent of an atomic theory for spectra it became clear that spectral lines were emitted when an atom made a transition between two different energy levels. It is while assigning the observed lines to the theoretically expected transitions that people borrowed labels like s, p, and d. Actually, spectroscopic notation can be quite bewildering to a novice although experts don't think so. In the early days when the subject was still developing, the notation was not stable and was itself evolving which created problems; now it has stabilized. Fortunately, we don't have to get lost in that jungle!

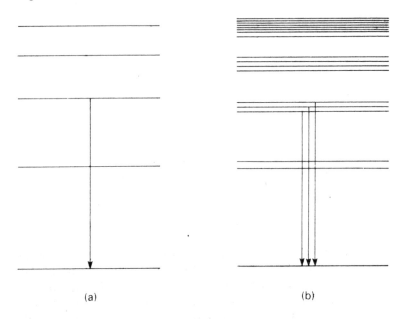

(a)   (b)

Fig.2.5 (a) shows schematically the energy levels in the Bohr model while (b) shows the modification introduced by the Sommerfeld model. Thus, what appears as single lines in the Bohr model manifests as a cluster of closely-spaced lines in the Sommerfeld model. This clustering is referred to as fine structure and became evident when the resolution of spectroscopes improved.

The Sommerfeld model gave a useful pointer to Bohr who was then trying to see how the electrons in complex atoms were organized into orbits. Actually, there were two things which guided Bohr. As mentioned, the first of course was the Sommerfeld model; the second was a remarkable empirical law discovered by Rydberg who noticed that the atomic number Z of the inert gases, namely helium, neon, argon, krypton, xenon and radon obeyed the following rule:

He $Z = 2 = 2.1^2$

Ne $Z = 10 = 2(1^2 + 2^2)$

Ar $Z = 18 = 2(1^2 + 2^2 + 2^2)$

Kr $Z = 36 = 2(1^2 + 2^2 + 2^2 + 3^2)$

Xe $Z = 54 = 2(1^2 + 2^2 + 2^2 + 3^2 + 3^2)$

Rn $Z = 86 = 2(1^2 + 2^2 + 2^2 + 3^2 + 3^2 + 4^2).$

Bohr interpreted this to mean: (i) The electrons were arranged in shells, and (ii) when the shells are fully occupied with electrons, the atom becomes inert as in the case of helium, etc. Supporting evidence for all this came from Moseley's results on the X-ray spectra of elements. Putting everything together, Bohr came up with his *auf-banprinzip*, which is essentially a model for how the electrons are arranged in shells around the nucleus. By and large this picture has survived with some modifications called for by the discovery of electron spin (see *Bose and His Statistics*). To cut a long story short, the present situation can be summarised via Fig.2.6 and Table 2.1.

Roughly, one can visualize shells which are the equivalent of Sommerfeld's orbit families. You must of course remember that this is a highly schematic (though convenient) picture because according to quantum mechanics, we really can't speak of orbits (see *The Quantum Revolution:* Part I). But we certainly can say that an electron assigned to an "inner" shell will have a greater probability of being closer to the nucleus than an electron in an "outer" shell.

Now why all this? Because this enables us to understand why and how the spectra of different atoms are different in some cases and appear similar in other cases. As an illustration, consider hydrogen and helium — see Fig.2.6. The neutral hydrogen atom has only one electron in the 1s shell whereas helium has two electrons; in fact in helium the 1s shell is full. Thus the spectra of the two elements are quite different. Now suppose one of the electrons in helium is

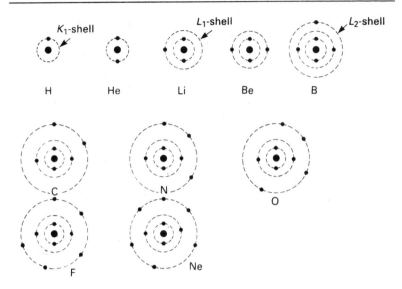

Fig.2.6 Schematic of the electron shells and their occupancy for the first few elements of the periodic table. The shells have been labelled using X-ray spectroscopic labels. Actually, L, M, ... shells have subshells inside them but they are not shown here. See, however, Table 2.1 and Fig.2.8.

somehow knocked out — obviously this would require a minimum amount of energy called the binding energy (see *Why Are Things the Way They Are ?*) — then one has an ionized helium atom, usually denoted He^+ or He II. One might expect the spectrum of He II to be similar to that of hydrogen, and indeed it is so. In fact, this is easy to see using the Bohr atom model, according to which the spectral frequencies of an atom with just one electron are given by

$$\nu_{mn} = R\left(\frac{1}{n^2} - \frac{1}{m^2}\right) \tag{2.4}$$

where R, called the Rydberg constant, is given by

$$R = \frac{2\pi m Z^2 e^4}{(1 + m/M)}, \tag{2.5}$$

Ze being the nuclear charge, m the mass of the electron and M that of the nucleus.

In physics as well as in astrophysics, one is interested in the spectra of all elements. However, for our purpose, which is to understand Saha's work and the impact that it made, it is enough to

Table 2.1 Organisation of the electrons into shells for the first few elements in the periodic table. Both atomic and X-ray spectroscopic labels have been used. Notice the shell closing in the case of He, Ne and Ar. Observe also how the 3d shell is first skipped and then later populated. Compare also with Fig.2.6.

	1s K_1 2	2s L_1 2	2p L_2 (L_{21},L_{22}) 6	3s M_1 2	3p M_2 (M_{21}, M_{22}) 6	3d M_3 (M_{32}, M_{33}) 10	4s N_1 2
H	1						
He	2						
Li	2	1					
Be	2	2					
B	2	2	1				
C	2	2	2				
N	2	2	3				
O	2	2	4				
F	2	2	5				
Ne	2	2	6				
Na	2	2	6	1			
Mg	2	2	6	2			
Al	2	2	6	2	1		
Si	2	2	6	2	2		
P	2	2	6	2	3		
S	2	2	6	2	4		
Cl	2	2	6	2	5		
Ar	2	2	6	2	6		
K	2	2	6	2	6	-	1
Ca	2	2	6	2	6	-	2
Sc	2	2	6	2	6	1	2
Tu	2	2	6	2	6	2	2
V	2	2	6	2	6	3	2
Cr	2	2	6	2	6	5	1

consider a few simple cases like the alkali metals (e.g., sodium) and the alkali-earth metals (e.g., calcium). Let us start with the sodium atom whose electronic configuration is: K_1 shell — 2 electrons, L_1 shell — 2 electrons, L_{21}, L_{22} shells (together) — 6 electrons and M_1 shell — 1 electron. The M_1 shell can actually accommodate two electrons but in sodium this shell is only partially occupied. Now suppose energy is supplied to the sodium atom so that it becomes excited, i.e., the atom goes to higher excited states. The simplest way in which this can happen is for the outermost electron to leave the M_1 shell and go to M_2, M_3, N_1, N_2, ..., etc. And when the electron so promoted returns to the M_1 shell a spectral line is emitted. Let us now consider the spectrum of sodium. Many lines are seen, and they occur in pairs as sketched in Fig.2.7. How are we to understand these in terms of the various possible electron· transitions? The first thing we must note here is that when the electron moves up to a higher energy state, it just can't jump from there to any unoccupied energy state below. Only certain transitions known as allowed transitions are permitted and they are governed by what are called *selection rules*.

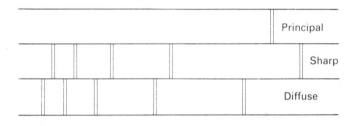

Principal

Sharp

Diffuse

Fig.2.7 Schematic of the spectrum of sodium. The lines occur in pairs, and from their appearance have been arranged into groups which are labelled sharp and diffuse. The D lines do not belong to either of these groups but form the leading lines of another series called the principal series. In principle, even hydrogen should show such a pair structure but the lines appear single due to very small separation.

What about an energy-level diagram which helps us to understand the spectrum sketched in Fig.2.7? There is one, a part of which is given in Fig.2.8. To understand this figure we must first consult Fig.2.9 which shows the so-called structure diagram. Notice the diagonal lines. If you consider the slots K_1, L_1, M_1, ... and refer back to Table 2.1, you will observe that all these refer to the electron being in the s-state; similarly M_2, N_2, ... refer to the p-state, M_3, N_3, O_3, ... to the d-state and so on. As I told you earlier, spectroscopy is rich in notation — which is quite confusing at times but unfortunately a necessity. We shall not stray too much into this business but merely note that K_1, L_1, M_1, ... are generically referred to as the ^2S states; similarly, M_2, N_2, ... are referred to as ^2P states and M_3, N_3, ... as ^2D states. It is on this that Fig.2.8 is based. This figure has two parts of which (a) is a simplified one. Guided by this you would think that the different spectral lines are all singlets,

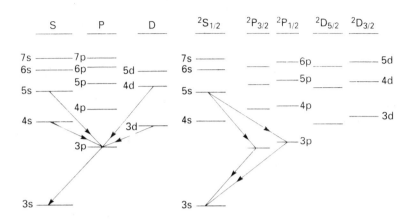

Fig.2.8 Schematic of the energy levels of sodium. Since the outermost electron is in the 3s-state, only that and the levels above it are shown. (a) shows the energy levels in low resolution. With higher resolution, the situation becomes changed as in (b). A few sample transitions are indicated from which we see how, in scheme (b), doublets emerge. This is basically due to the subshells structure present in shells L, M, ...

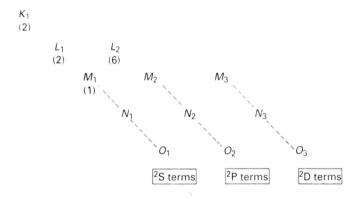

Fig.2.9 Structure diagram of sodium. Displayed here is the hierarchy of subshells labelled in the X-ray term notation. In the normal atom, subshells upto M_1 are occupied while all others are empty. The solitary electron in M_1 can pick up energy and go to other states like M_2, M_3, ... , N_1, N_2, ... , etc. The diagonal arrangement shows the ^{2}S, ^{2}P and ^{2}D terms conveniently. This is how Saha illustrated the structure.

whereas from Fig.2.7 we know that one actually observes doublets. Why is this so? The answer lies in the fact that the ^{2}P and ^{2}D

states are not singlets but actually denote a pair of states — in the case of ^2P it is $^2P_{1/2}$ and $^2P_{3/2}$, while in the case of ^2D it is $^2D_{3/2}$ and $^2D_{5/2}$. This doubling arises because the L_2, M_2, N_2, ... shells on the one hand and the M_3, N_3, O_3, ... shells on the other have internal compartments. Once the doublet nature of the ^2P and ^2D states is recognised, the single lines of Fig.2.8 (a) become double lines as explicitly illustrated in Fig.2.10 for the famous D lines of sodium.

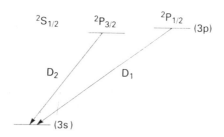

Fig.2.10 Portion of the energy-level diagram of sodium, relevant to the origin of the famous D lines.

To sum up the sodium story, we have the following rules:

Series	Transitions
Principal	$(^2P_{1/2}, \,^2P_{3/2}) \rightarrow {}^2S_{1/2}$
Sharp	$^2S_{1/2} \rightarrow (^2P_{1/2}, \,^2P_{3/2})$
Diffuse	$(^2D_{3/2}, \,^2D_{5/2}) \rightarrow (^2P_{1/2}, \,^2P_{3/2})$

So much for sodium. Remember that what applies to sodium applies also to the other alkali metals, i.e., cesium, rubidium, etc.

Next we turn to calcium, for that would figure prominently later. Calcium (Ca) is the element next to potassium (K) which is an alkali metal. The outermost shell of Ca is 4s, and it has its full complement of two electrons. This is the case for the neutral calcium atom, denoted Ca I. Suppose one of these electrons is knocked off so that the calcium atom becomes ionized — denoted Ca^+ or Ca II. In this case, the electronic structure (of Ca II) is the same as that of neutral potassium. In other words, we may expect a similarity in the spectra of Ca II and K and indeed other alkali metals as well.

At this stage the game becomes interesting. You should sit with a periodic table and imagine knocking off electrons from the outer shell of neutral atoms and ask: Which neutral atom's spectrum would correspond to the spectrum of the ionised atom under consideration? If you do this, you would come to conclusions like:

Spectra of Mg^+, Al^{++}, Si^{+++} (or, if you prefer, Mg II, Al III, Si IV) must resemble that of Na.

Spectra of Al^+, Si^{++}, P^{+++} must be similar to that of Mg, and so on.

This rule was discovered about seventy years ago, and is known as the Sommerfeld–Kossel displacement law. As you can see, it makes sense once we understand how spectra originate.

Now what has all this got to do with Saha's discovery? Ah, for that you have to go through the next two chapters!

3 *The Sun God's Mysterious Story*

Twinkle, twinkle little star,
How I wonder what you are.

So goes the nursery rhyme. Have you ever wondered about stars? Even if you have, have you ever wondered how we have been able to obtain *so much* information about these wonderful objects which are all *so far, far* away? If you have, you should be amazed because everything we have learnt about stars is simply by *looking* at them! In this and the next two chapters, I shall tell you a portion of this fascinating story, i.e., the part that deals with Saha's discovery.

Among the stars, the Sun is very special and you know why. People have been observing the Sun for ages but it was only during the last century that information gathering was stepped up, which was possible due to the invention of many instruments. The first step was taken by Fraunhofer (see Box 3.1) who, emulating Newton, examined the solar spectrum but while doing so, made some improvements to Newton's arrangement as described in the previous chapter. Straightaway this paid dividends, for Fraunhofer found that the continuous spectrum discovered by Newton was actually crossed by numerous dark lines, now known as *Fraunhofer lines*. Today we can resolve 20,000 or more of these lines but with his resolution, Fraunhofer saw only about 500. Even this was a great surprise. Fraunhofer did not know what caused these lines but he instinctively knew that they were important. So he used a grating and patiently measured their frequencies, catalogued them and denoted the more prominent bands by the letters of alphabet as below:

A B C D   E F   G   H K

red   yellow green violet beyond violet

As Saha has remarked, "these black lines are the hieroglyphics in which the Sun-God has written his own story." Fraunhofer did not stop with the Sun; he turned his spectroscope towards the stars as well and found that their spectra also had dark lines; clearly they too had stories of their own to tell.

Box 3.1 Joseph von Fraunhofer was born in Germany in 1787. An orphan, he earned a living by becoming at an early age, an apprentice to a mirror maker. He spent his meagre earnings for buying books, and taught himself many subjects like geometry. In 1801, two houses in Munich collapsed. Fraunhofer was living in one of these and he was the only one who escaped being buried alive. Soon after this, Fraunhofer mastered optics and was invited to work with a leading manufacturer of optical instruments. Here he acquired a great reputation not only as an expert craftsman but also as a skilled designer of optical instruments. He also perfected a method of producing high quality glass. Fraunhofer is of course best remembered for his discovery (in 1814) of the dark lines in the solar spectrum, but few knew that he used these lines as reference points for the measurement of refractive indices. His other great achievement was the measurement of the wavelength of the optical spectrum. He not only invented the spectroscope but built many fine instruments for various observatories. So great was his reputation that astronomers considered it a privilege to have their orders accepted by him. He died in 1826.

Several decades passed before Kirchhoff and Bunsen came up with an explanation for the dark lines discovered by Fraunhofer. Essentially it was the following: The core of the Sun is very hot and emits radiation at all frequencies, i.e., the spectrum is continuous. On the way out, this light naturally has to pass through the outer layers of the Sun or the solar atmosphere. Present here are various species of atoms and they selectively absorb radiation of certain frequencies. It is this absorption which is responsible for the dark lines as Figs.3.1 and 3.2 explain in slightly greater detail.

Kirchhoff's discovery was a tremendous step forward (see Box 3.2). Just as an atom can be tagged or identified by its emission lines, it can likewise be identified by its absorption lines — and Fraunhofer lines are nothing but absorption lines. In short, the dark lines in the spectra of the Sun and the stars tell us something about the atoms present in the outer atmosphere of these objects. As Saha put it, "Besides spectrum analysis, Kirchhoff's great work gave birth to the present science of Astrophysics, or the Physics of the Sun and the heavenly bodies."

At this stage let us focus on the Sun and consider other stars later. To us the Sun appears as a dazzling disc but actually it has a

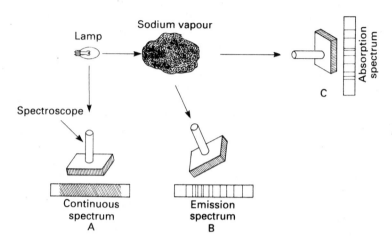

Fig.3.1 Illustration of the spectra observable under different conditions. The heated filament lamp gives a continuous spectrum. If the light from the lamp is passed through sodium vapour, some of the incident light can be absorbed by the atoms, raising them to excited states of energy. When the atoms deexcite they emit characteristic frequencies which form the emission spectrum. When the light from the lamp is observed after being allowed to pass through a thick layer of sodium vapour, the spectrum will not appear continuous as at A but will have dark lines superposed against a continuous background. These dark lines correspond to transitions in sodium excited by the radiation incident on it.

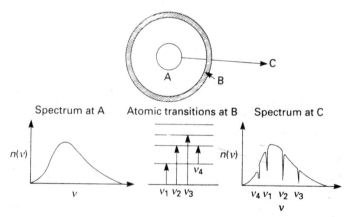

Fig.3.2 This figure amplifies the previous one and illustrates how the continuous spectrum originating from the photosphere A is modified by the atomic (absorption) transitions in the chromosphere B to produce the Fraunhofer spectrum at C.

Box 3.2 Gustav Robert Kirchhoff was born in 1824 in Germany. His great claim to fame is the discovery he made in 1859 along with Robert Bunsen (of Bunsen burner fame). For years, people had been studying spectra emitted by different substances when introduced into a flame. Everyone knew that there was some connection between the bright lines seen in such emissions and the dark lines discovered by Fraunhofer in the Sun's continuous spectrum, but what exactly the connection was, no one knew. Kirchhoff and Bunsen provided the answer. Actually it came out of a larger study of why and how hot bodies emit radiation and absorb radiation. Kirchhoff observed that if a body can emit radiation at a particular wavelength λ, it can also absorb radiation at the same wavelength. In fact, the ratio of the emissive and absorptive powers of a body depend only on the (absolute) temperature of the body and not on its composition or nature. Kirchhoff's law also implies that if a body is completely opaque, i.e., black, then, when heated, the body would emit radiation at *all* wavelengths. That is why one often speaks of the Sun as a blackbody. But if a body is not perfectly black, then it can emit and absorb radiation only at a finite number of frequencies. This is particularly true of gases. Extending the argument, Kirchhoff and Bunsen concluded that "the dark lines of the solar spectrum which are not caused by terrestrial atmosphere, arise from the presence in the glowing solar atmosphere of these substances which, in a flame, produce bright lines in the same position."

Kirchhoff and Bunsen became celebrities overnight. Scientific spectroscopy was born and soon proved to be a magic key to a great number of practical discoveries. Half a century later, it ushered in the era of modern atomic physics. Kirchhoff died in 1887.

complex structure, a simplified description of which is given in Figs. 3.3–3.5 (see also Box 3.3). Deep inside is the core where energy production occurs due to nuclear reactions (see *Chandrasekhar and His Limit*). This energy then flows outside and near the outer surface, produces turbulence and convection cells (see *The Many Phases of Matter*). Thanks to this, the surface of the Sun presents a mottled appearance when examined with a telescope having a good revolving power. What we see when we observe the Sun is really the outer surface or the *photosphere*. The tenuous atmospheric layer beyond this is called the *chromosphere* and beyond that is the *corona*. On account of the dazzle of the Sun, one cannot readily see and examine these outer regions, unless special measures are taken. Till the middle of the last century, people did not have such tricks and the only time the chromosphere and the corona were visible was during a total solar eclipse.

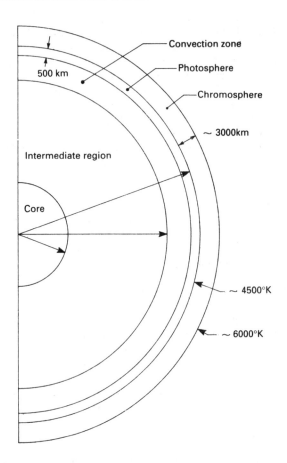

Fig.3.3 Schematic cross section of the Sun showing the important layers.

Story within a story (!), and we now switch to the fascinating saga of total solar eclipses. The total solar eclipse has been described as "probably the most magnificent sight in all Nature." I saw a total solar eclipse in 1980 and can assure you that this is indeed the case. I am sure you know how an eclipse occurs but even so, it may be useful to brush up on a few facts.

In astronomy, an eclipse is generally said to occur when one celestial body enters the shadow of another body, or when it is hidden partially or wholly by another body. However, many cases can be distinguished and the term eclipse is mostly used in one particular situation. Our Moon covers or hides many stars as it moves in the sky. In all such cases the word eclipse is not used on account of the wide disparity between the *apparent* sizes. If a

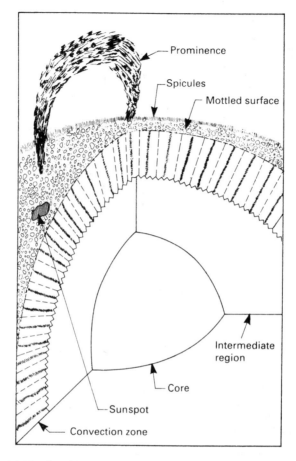

Fig.3.4 A highly simplified cut-away view of the Sun, showing the interior. Notice (a) the mottled surface which arises due to the formation of convection zones, (b) the sunspot, (c) the spicules and (d) prominence.

"small" body passes in front of a "large" body one speaks of a *transit*, whereas if it is the other way round one has an *occultation* — see Fig.3.6. The eclipse is the specific event involving the Earth, the Sun and the Moon. As you know, the Earth moves around the Sun in an elliptic orbit — see Fig.3.7. Let us take the plane of orbital motion of the Earth as the reference plane. Just as the Earth moves around the Sun, the Moon orbits the Earth and its orbit is inclined to the reference plane (by about 5°). The points at which the Moon's orbit crosses the reference plane are called *nodes*. As the Moon orbits the Earth we have the familiar new moon and the full moon phenomena. When the new moon occurs

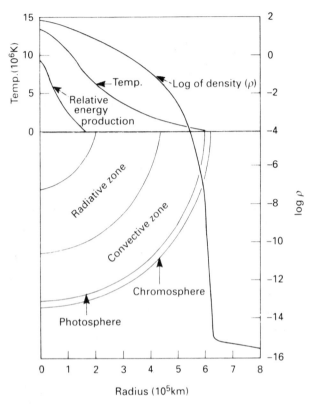

Fig.3.5 Variation of some of the parameters relating to the Sun, as one moves away from the interior outwards.

Box 3.3 This box supplements information given in the text about the Sun.

The centre of the Sun is very dense ($\sim 90\text{g/cm}^3$) and the temperature is $\sim 20 \times 10^6$ **K**. Heat is produced by thermonuclear reactions. Thanks to the high density, the material at the centre is opaque — a few millimetres are enough to absorb light. However, photons are also reemitted and in this way heat and light are transported outwards. In the centre there are no ions or neutral atoms — only electrons and nuclei. Therefore, most of the absorption of radiation is by continuous processes such as the scattering of light by electrons.

As one moves away from the centre the temperature comes down, making it possible for ions and even neutral atoms to exist. New absorption mechanisms take over and there results a steep temperature gradient. It is this which leads to convection cells and finally a mottled appearance on the surface. What we see is this surface, and it is called the photosphere.

There are gases above the photosphere and they form the Sun's atmosphere. However, the density is much lower than in the case of the Earth (can you guess why?). The Sun's atmosphere has a glow of its own owing to the emission of light by the atoms there, but this glow is not seen on account of the brilliant dazzle of the photosphere. It becomes visible only at the time of a total solar eclipse, and because of its red colour this layer is referred to as the chromosphere. This is the region where the Fraunhofer lines are produced.

The upper part of the chromosphere is not uniform and there are numerous jets called *spicules*. Apart from these there are huge flames which shoot out once in a while. They are called *prominences*.

Beyond the chromosphere lies the solar *corona*. It is very extensive and has no sharp boundary. It simply thins out into space. The corona has a very high temperature and is the source of radio emission from the Sun. High temperature does not mean that the corona is a huge reservoir of heat — just that particles there have exceedingly high velocities.

Visible on the photospheric disc are some dark regions which are referred to as *sunspots*. They appear to be holes in which gases are whirling around. These regions are about 2000°C cooler than the neighbouring areas and therefore appear dark.

Some vital statistics

Radius	$\sim 7 \times 10^5$ km
Mass	$\sim 2 \times 10^{33}$ g
Mean density	~ 1.4 g/cm^3
Surface gravity	$\sim 2.7 \times 10^4$ cm/s^2
Total power output	$\sim 3.9 \times 10^{26}$ W
Period of rotation	~ 27 days
Mean distance from Earth	$\sim 1.5 \times 10^8$ km

close to a node, there is an eclipse. Now the angle subtended by the Sun and the Moon at the Earth are very nearly the same. Thus, when the new moon occurs exactly at a node (or very near to it), one has a total solar eclipse — see Fig.3.8.

Solar eclipses aren't all that frequent. True, ninety such eclipses are supposed to occur in this century but we in India did not see any during the first half of the century. The first one visible in this country occurred in 1955 and the next one came in 1980. But we are in luck, for this grand event is scheduled to be visible again in India on October 24, 1995 and on August 11, 1999. Watch out, and pray hard for clear skies on both those days!

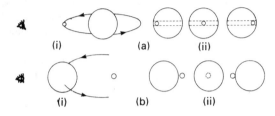

Fig.3.6 (a) illustrates transit which is said to occur when a small celestial object crosses in front of a larger one. Note that small and large refer to angular diameters. The various stages of the transit are shown in a(ii). (b) shows occultation which occurs when a big object passes in front of a smaller one.

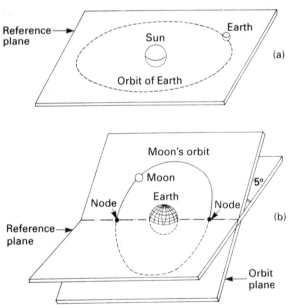

Fig.3.7 (a) shows the orbit of the Earth around the Sun. We shall take this as the reference plane. (Strictly speaking it is the plane of the ecliptic which is the reference plane. Find out what it is!) (b) shows the orbit of the Moon around the Earth. The plane of the Moon's orbit is tilted by about 5° with respect to the reference plane. The two points where the Moon's orbit cuts the reference plane are referred to as nodes.

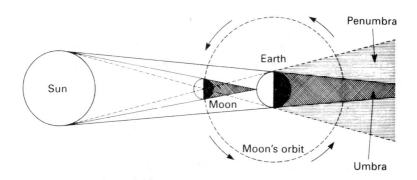

Fig.3.8 Relative dispositions of the Sun, the Moon and the Earth at the time of a total solar eclipse.

Figures 3.9–3.11 give some more details about the occurrence of the eclipse and its nature. From the point of view of solar physics, the total solar eclipse is very important because that is when the chromosphere and the corona become visible. The duration of the totality can be anything from 0 to a maximum of 9 minutes. All observations made during a total eclipse must therefore be crammed into that short period!

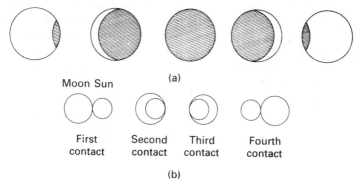

Fig.3.9 (a) shows a schematic of the appearance of a total solar eclipse during the various stages. Compare with the figure on the book cover. The eclipse arises when the Moon crosses in front of the Sun. The angular diameters of the Sun and the Moon (as seen from the Earth) are nearly the same. However, depending on the circumstances, the Moon may appear to be slightly bigger or smaller than the Sun. In the former case a total eclipse is possible. As shown in (b), the eclipse begins at first contact, goes through various stages [as in (a)] and ends at fourth contact. Totality is the period between the second and the third contact. This duration is quite small.

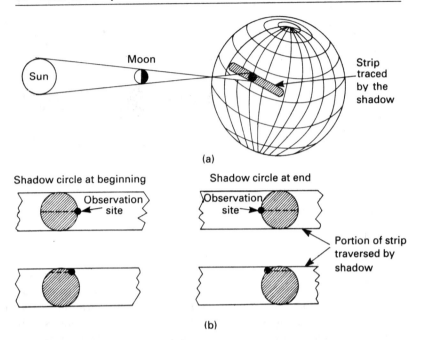

(a)

(b)

Fig.3.10 At the time of a total solar eclipse, the Moon casts a shadow about 200 km in diameter. This dark spot moves and traces a strip and totality would be visible only to people in this strip. The duration of totality depends on where the observation site is located with respect to the strip. As can be seen from (b), if the site is favourably located, the shadow will take a relatively longer time to cross. If it is at the edge, the transit of the shadow will be rapid.

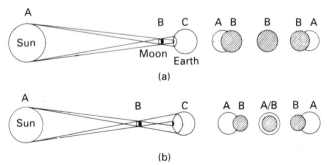

Fig.3.11 As mentioned earlier, depending on the circumstance, the Moon can appear to be slightly bigger or smaller than the Sun. In the former case, total solar eclipse occurs as shown in (a). In the latter case, an angular eclipse occurs as shown in (b). Study the appearances of the shadows in the two cases as B crosses A.

1-metre Vainu Bappu Telescope at Kavalur in Tamil Nadu.

100" telescope at Mt.Wilson in America.

Hubble Space Telescope launched into orbit around the Earth by America.

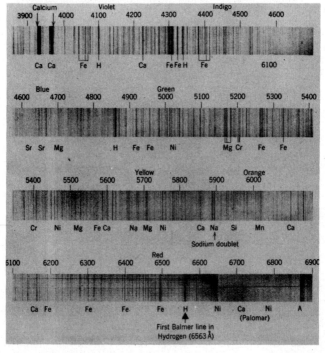

Fraunhofer lines in the solar spectrum.

Hζ *K H*   SrIIHδ   Hγ   HeI   Hβ
    ‾Ca II‾   4077   4471

A typical flash spectrum recorded during a total solar eclipse.

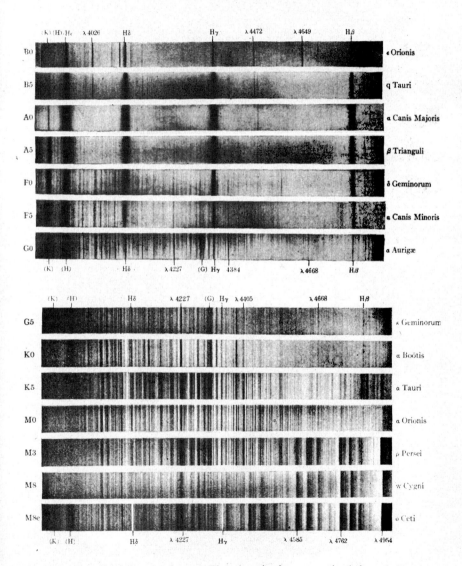

Spectra of various classes of stars. The class is shown on the left and the
name of the star on the right.

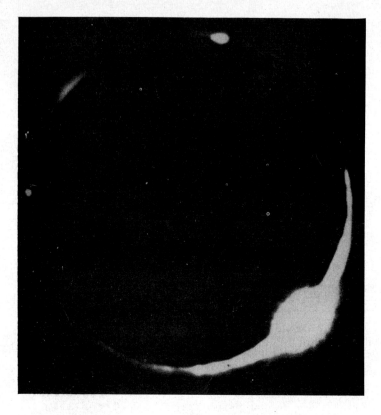

"Diamond Ring Effect" seen at the end of totality.

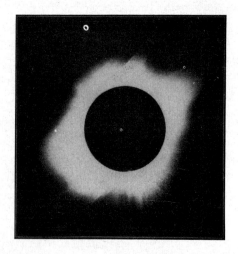

Corona seen during a total solar eclipse.

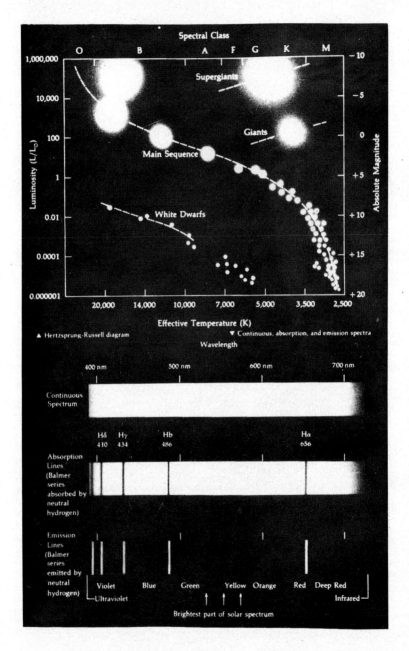

This collage shows the H–R diagram at the top and various types of spectra at the bottom.

The cyclotron constructed by Saha.

The practice of arranging expeditions to observe total solar eclipses started in 1842. That was when the solar corona was first observed which Bailey described as follows:

> The dark body of the Moon was suddenly surrounded with a corona or a kind of bright glory similar in shape and relative magnitude to that which painters draw around the head of saints and called by the French an aureole ... But the most remarkable aspect attending the phenomenon was the appearance of three large protuberances apparently emanating from the circumference of the Moon, but evidently forming a part of the corona.

These protuberances are now called solar *prominences*, and extend to great heights above the chromosphere. The eclipse of 1851 is noteworthy because for the first time, a photographic record was made of the eclipse. The solar eclipse of 1868 has a special significance for a number of reasons (see Boxes 3.4 and 3.5). India was the scene of action and for the first time, spectra were recorded of the light emitted by the chromosphere. And this time, instead of dark lines against a bright background (i.e., Fraunhofer spectrum), a series of *bright* lines were seen as in the usual emission spectra recorded in the laboratory. This was referred to as the *flash spectrum* because it was visible only for a short period. Actually, Young had visually observed the flash spectrum even during the eclipse of 1851 but he did not make a photographic record. There was some doubt as to whether or not the flash spectrum was an exact reversal of the Fraunhofer spectrum. The data obtained during the eclipse of 1868 did not quite settle this issue, and the resolution came during the eclipse of 1898 — again the scene of observation was India, and the two prominent observers were Lockyer (see Boxes 3.6 and 3.7) and Evershed (see Box 3.8).

Let us now look more closely at the flash spectrum for that was what got people excited about the nature of the chromosphere and led to all sorts of speculations. Figure 3.12(a) shows a rough schematic of how the flash spectrum is observed, while Fig.3.12(b) gives some idea of what the spectrum looks like. We see here many lines. Why is it they appear curved, unlike the Fraunhofer lines which appear straight? Because while recording the flash spectrum, the slit of the spectrograph is dispensed with and one directly observes the bright ring around the Sun. Figure 3.13 shows a sketch of the solar chromosphere. Since the Moon comes in the way (during an eclipse), only the crescent-like portion ABCDEFA is observed. Present in this are various elements. Let us say the different elements are present upto different heights (see Fig. 3.13). We may thus assign

Box 3.4 One important event associated with the eclipse of 1868 is the discovery of helium. The discovery of helium is a story full of drama. It begins in 1866 when Lockyer started his effort to observe the solar chromosphere on an ordinary day. He took over two years to develop and perfect such an instrument (see Box 3.5). Meanwhile there occurred on August 18, 1868 a total solar eclipse which could be observed in India. Lockyer stayed back in London but sent his representative to India. Finally, in mid-October 1868, Lockyer did succeed in recording the spectrum of the solar chromosphere on a normal day. He presented a report to the Royal Society of London on October 23, and the news was promptly conveyed by the Secretary of the Royal Society to Warren de La Rue, the Secretary of the French Academy. La Rue received the news about Lockyer's achievement on October 26.

Meanwhile, in far away Guntur (in Andhra Pradesh), the noted French astronomer Janssen recorded a spectrum of a solar prominence during the eclipse on August 18. Janssen wanted to confirm his data but the next total solar eclipse was years away. Applying his mind, Janssen invented a method which was practically the same as that devised by Lockyer. Janssen was so happy that he sent a cable to the French Academy saying: "We have total solar eclipse for the whole day". Janssen stayed back in Guntur continuing his observations for another seventeen days. He then analysed his results and cabled his findings to the French Academy. By sheer coincidence, Janssen's report was also received on October 23, in fact within a few minutes of that from Lockyer.

There was now the question of priority. The French Government acted wisely and decided to honour both. It struck a special medal containing on one side the profiles of both Lockyer and Janssen and on the other, the Sun-God in a chariot drawn by four horses, below which was the inscription: "Analyse des Protuberances Solaires, 18 Aout, 1868."

The story does not end here. In the spectrum recorded by Janssen during the eclipse was a yellow line termed D_3. Janssen did not pay much attention to it but this D_3 line caught Lockyer's attention. Lockyer continued his investigations and in November he came to the conclusion that the D_3 line was caused by a substance NOT known on Earth. He called the substance *helium*, deriving the word from the Greek *helios* (meaning Sun).

In 1891, Hillebrand of the U.S. Geological Survey heated a sample of uranium oxide and examined the spectra of the gases evolved. He saw many strange lines but could not explain them. In 1895, Sir William Ramsay (who was then in search of argon) heated a mineral containing uranium. Investigating the spectra of gases evolved, Ramsay found argon as he expected to, but in addition saw a bright yellow line. At his request Sir William Crooke measured the wavelength of this yellow line which was the same as that of the D_3 line seen in the solar spectrum. Ramsay thus showed that helium occurred on Earth also. This finding was communicated simultaneously to the Royal Society of London and to the French Academy on March 26, 1895.

For more about Lockyer, see Box 3.6.

Box 3.5 As I have explained, an eclipse is produced when the Moon covers the Sun. From the astrophysical point of view, the eclipse is important for that is when we can see the chromosphere and the corona and make observations. Now if it is only a question of covering the Sun, why do we need the Moon? Why can't we do it ourselves? All one has to do is to hold a coin in front of the eye and adjust the distance so that the coin masks the photosphere — see Fig.(a). If we can do that, we don't have to wait around for the eclipse.

In principle this is fine but in practice there is a problem. Essentially it is due to glare, i.e., stray light scattered by dust etc. But, if sufficient care is taken, the Sun's photosphere *can* be masked on any day and the arrangement used is as sketched in Fig.(b). Such an instrument was devised by Lyot in France in 1931. This enables one to study the corona, etc., even on normal days.

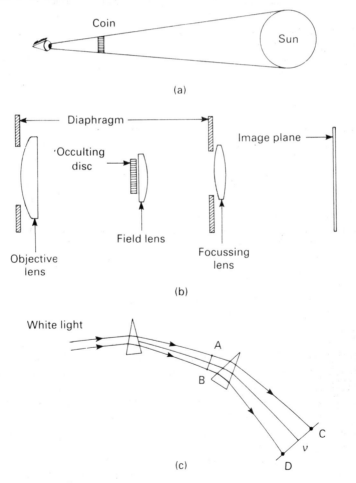

Roughly sixty years prior to this, Lockyer and Janssen developed a technique for observing the spectra of solar prominences. The general idea may be understood from the schematic in Fig.(c). One directs a spectroscope at the edge of the Sun's disc. Of course, a lot of stray light could get in but by careful design this can be minimized. Even so, there is the powerful continuous spectrum to contend with. Lockyer tackled the latter by adding several dispersing prisms one behind the other in tandem. They essentially spread out the continuous spectrum. For example if AB in Fig.(c) is 3 cm, CD is 6 cm and so on. So the intensity originally spread over 3 cm is now spread over 6 cm, making the intensity weaker. Added to this is absorption which also helps. In short, the background against which a particular spectral line of frequency say ν, is to be viewed becomes weaker. Notice, the spectral line being monochromatic, does not suffer that much reduction.

Multiple dispersion is no doubt a clever way of fighting the background but where exactly on the Sun's periphery does one look for a prominence? That was a chancy affair, at least to start with, and that is why Lockyer took quite some time to develop the technique. Janssen was luckier. Thanks to the eclipse data, he knew roughly where to look.

Box 3.6 Joseph Norman Lockyer (later Sir Norman Lockyer) was born in England in 1836. He drifted into science mainly as an amateur astronomer. This led to his appointment as the Director of the Solar Physical Laboratory in London, a post he occupied till the observatory was shifted to Cambridge in 1911. Lockyer started his career just about the time Kirchhoff made his great discovery. Excited by it, Lockyer attached a spectroscope to his telescope. In those days, one had to wait for a total solar eclipse in order to make good observations of the chromosphere. But Lockyer was not prepared to wait for such occasional events. He applied his mind and invented a technique whereby one could record spectra of the chromosphere even on a non-eclipse day — a tale already told in Box 3.5.

Lockyer was always daring and did not hesitate to put forth radical ideas even if they met with a lot of criticism. One such was his theory of inorganic evolution. Though wrong in details, it approached the problem in the right spirit. Another bold idea of his was the meteorite hypothesis. He believed that "all self-luminous bodies in the celestial spaces are composed either of swarms of meteorites or of masses of meteoric vapour produced by heat". Starting from this idea, he developed an elaborate picture of the origin and the evolution of nebulae and stars. In effect his theory implied that a star began its life as a cold body, became hot, rose to a maximum temperature and then cooled off again. However, the prevailing opinion was that the star was born hot and gradually cooled off. But Lockyer held that though both the young and the old stars were cold (as indicated by their spectra), their densities were very different. Later work by Russell showed that stellar evolution indeed followed such a sequence and that both young and old stars were cold — today we would call them giant and dwarf respectively which, incidentally, also indicates how much they differ in density. Commenting on Lockyer's daring, Saha once wrote:

> His lot was like that of Icarus who in trying to fly to the Sun with wings of wax, had to end by falling into the sea; while lesser men, confining their flights like the prudent Daedalus to the sea level, had a happy and comfortable journey. But for the progress of science, Icarus's flights are more fruitful because they bring to our view fresh lands and sights ...

Lockyer was one of the first to recognize a connection between the sunspot cycle and meteorological activity. Perhaps his most lasting achievement was the founding of the famous journal *Nature*. He was its editor for fifty years! Lockyer died in 1920 (the very year when Saha gave his theory).

For more about Daedalus and Icarus, see Box 3.7.

Box 3.7 Here is some more about Daedalus and Icarus. Daedalus was an inventor who worked for King Minos of Crete (an island in the Mediterranean). One of Daedalus's famous inventions was the Labyrinth, a place with so many passageways that one could get lost for ever. It was designed as a prison for a monster called Minotaur. A Prince named Theseus slew the monster and Daedalus helped the Prince to elope with the King's daughter. Naturally the King became furious and he threw both Daedalus and his son Icarus into the Labyrinth.

Daedalus knew how to get out of the Labyrinth but his problem did not stop there; he had to escape from the island itself. So Daedalus made two pairs of wings using feathers, wax and thread. One day the father and the son stole out of the Labyrinth and went to the top of the hill. They strapped on the wings and by flapping them, rose into the air. Soon they were flying over the sea. Icarus was so thrilled that he began to go higher and higher, despite warnings by Daedalus. Alas, the heat of the Sun melted the wax, and the feathers came off. The wings disintegrated and Icarus fell with a thud into the sea and got drowned. Daedalus, on the other hand, was prudent and by maintaining a low altitude was able to cross the sea and make good his escape.

Can a man actually fly by strapping on wings? Mathematicians have analysed this problem. Try to find out what conclusion they reached!

Box 3.8 John Evershed was born in England in 1864. As a young man, he studied solar spectroscopy and carried out experiments on the emission and absorption spectra of gases. In this he was helped by a gift of equipment he received from one Ranyard, a distinguished amateur astronomer.

Evershed then worked as a spectrochemical assistant for an oil company in London. His employer appreciated Evershed's interest in astrophysics and gave him leave to go on several expeditions to observe total solar eclipses. Thus it was that he came to India in 1898 when he photographed for the first time, the Balmer series right down to the ultraviolet limit at 3646Å. Shortly after this, Evershed was appointed assistant to C. Michie Smith, the Director of the Madras and Kodaikanal Observatories.

A few words about how those observatories came into being. The earliest reference to the use of an astronomical telescope in India goes back to 1651 when one Jeremiah Shekerley made certain observations at Surat. Later the Jesuit priest Fr. Richard carried out more systematic studies at Pondicherry (where he was stationed), and in 1689 he even discovered a comet. The credit for establishing the first regular astronomical observatory goes to William Petrie who did so in Madras in the year 1786. Soon the East India Company took over this observatory as it was beneficial for its affairs. For many decades, the Madras observatory was the only professional observatory in the country carrying out astronomical observation through telescopes.

In 1876–77, there was a very severe drought in South India and a Commission of Enquiry was set up by the Government. Among other things, the Commission recommended that an observatory dedicated to solar observations alone be set up. By this time it was common knowledge that there was a connection between sunspot activity and meteorological factors, and it is this which possibly influenced the Commission's recommendation. Thanks to it, a solar observatory come up at Kodaikanal, and is functional even today.

In 1911, Evershed became the Director of the Madras and the Kodaikanal Observatories. He took full advantage of the location of Kodaikanal, designed and built many instruments and carried out detailed observations. One of his discoveries relating to sunspot activity has been named the Evershed effect. In 1915 he led an expedition to Kashmir to measure the red shift of spectral lines in connection with the verification of Einstein's theories.

Evershed retired in 1923 and returned to England where he continued astronomical observations but in a private capacity. He died in 1956.

occupation crescents to each of these elements as in the figure. And of course as different elements emit at different frequencies, the spectroscope resolves these frequencies and presents them as separated arcs. Depending on the presence in the chromosphere, the crescent is small or large. Correspondingly, in the flash spectrum one sees both small and large arcs. In fact, by carefully analysing the arcs on the photograph, one can estimate the heights to which the different elements are present in the chromosphere.

Going back to Fig.3.12, observe the two big arcs denoted by the letters H and K. These correspond exactly to the H and K bands

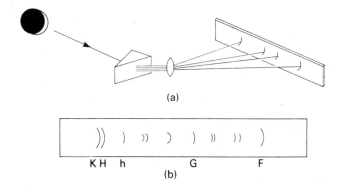

(a)

(b)

K H   h   G   F

Fig.3.12 (a) shows a schematic of how the chromosphere is observed during a total solar eclipse. The slit of the spectroscope is dispensed with and the entire chromosphere (or the portion visible) is viewed. If the chromosphere appears as a crescent, the lines in the flash spectrum also appear as crescents as shown in (b). Here the lines H and K are due to calcium, while h, G and F are due to hydrogen.

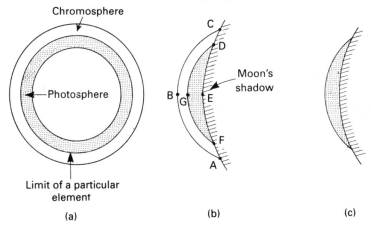

Fig.3.13 This figure explains why the curved lines in the flash spectrum have varying sizes. (a) shows a simplified version of the chromosphere and the height to which a certain element is present. Suppose only the crescent ABCDEFA is visible as shown in (b). The element concerned occupies the subcrescent DEFGD. This is shown separately in (c). Different elements being present up to different heights in the chromosphere will form different subcrescents. And each element has characteristic frequencies. Hence the flash spectrum has crescents of different sizes.

recorded by Fraunhofer. For quite some time, no one knew which particular element produced these lines. From an analysis of the arc dimensions it was estimated that this element, whatever it was, was present upto a height of 14,000 km, whereas hydrogen reached a height of only 8000 km. Thus, for a while there was the speculation that the H and K lines were due to an element lighter than hydrogen! But laboratory experiments soon dispelled this illusion and the twin lines were found to be due to calcium. But the matter did not end there. The question arose: How come the calcium atom which is 40 times more massive than the hydrogen atom is present up to a much greater height in the solar chromosphere than hydrogen is? Did gravity go on a holiday? Quite a crop of theories were proposed to explain this "anomaly". Many astronomers were of the opinion that there was a force of *levity* in the Sun which largely neutralised gravity. Saha tells us that one Prof. Julius even went to the extent of dismissing the whole set of eclipse phenomena — the chromosphere, the flash spectrum and the corona — as mere "optical illusions"! Meanwhile, people tried various experiments in the laboratory to shed light on this question, and the foremost among these was Norman Lockyer.

Now the spectrum of an element (calcium say) can be observed by introducing it into a flame or an arc or a spark. Lockyer found that even if the element was the same, the spectrum observed in the three cases varied substantially — see Fig.3.14. He then argued that the element experiences a *stimulus* when introduced into the flame etc., and that the spectrum of an element varies with stimulus. In the spark the stimulus is more and the lines are therefore *enhanced*. The H and K lines are the enhanced lines of calcium. Noting the fact that calcium extends to a height of about 14,000 km, Lockyer concluded that greater stimulus (whatever that is!) exists in the solar chromosphere than in the photosphere.

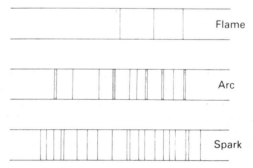

Fig.3.14 Emission spectra are often recorded by introducing a piece of the substance, e.g. calcium into a flame, or an arc or a spark. The spectra obtained in the different cases are quite different as the figure shows. Lockyer attributed this to varying stimulus. Today we would identify stimulus with the excitation of the atom.

What is this so-called stimulus, and why on earth should the atom respond in this strange manner to the stimulus? We are here talking of the last quarter of the last century and at that time, the belief was that the atom was the ultimate building block of matter, meaning that it could not be broken or divided further. Lockyer dared to defy this widely-held belief and proposed a theory called the *theory of inorganic evolution*. People were familiar with Darwin's theory of evolution but that applied to living beings (i.e., organic matter). And now Lockyer claimed that even inorganic matter went through an evolution of its own!

Naturally few took Lockyer seriously. But we must not likewise dismiss him summarily and instead pause to ask why he came up with such a theory. This is where stars and their spectra come into the picture. With the aid of the naked eye, it is possible to distinguish four classes of stars — white, yellow, yellow-red and deep-red. This classification is in the order of descending (surface) temperature, i.e., white stars have the highest temperatures and deep-red stars have the lowest. Lockyer carefully examined the spectra of stars and showed that the spectra of red and yellow-red stars are practically made up of low stimulus lines; the enhanced lines are only faintly present. But in white stars, the low stimulus lines become faint and the enhanced lines become more prominent. Lockyer immediately drew the following conclusions:

1. The stimulus really corresponds to temperature; the higher the temperature, the greater is the stimulus.
2. Stars evolve, and as they evolve their temperature goes down.
3. White stars are young stars. Their temperature is high, which is why they appear white. Deep-red stars are aged stars and their temperature is comparatively lower.
4. As the stars evolve, the elements present in them also evolve.
5. In the deep-red stars, calcium is evident via a line called the g line. In the lab, this is seen in flame spectra. This line is therefore a normal line (i.e., not enhanced) and originates from the normal calcium atom.
6. In white stars the g line is absent; instead the enhanced lines of calcium, i.e., the H and K lines are present.
7. Since the white star is a young star, the atom responsible for the H and K lines is a precursor to the normal calcium atom — Lockyer named this precursor atom *protocalcium*.

Arguing in this fashion, Lockyer suggested that the elements change with stimulus and assume their protoforms whenever the temperature is high. It is the *protoform* that gives rise to enhanced lines. And as the star gets older and cools off, the elements also evolve from their proto- to their normal forms.

Getting back to the Sun and the spectrum of its chromosphere, the situation even as late as 1919 was the following:

1. The chromosphere spectrum showed strong H and K lines (of calcium) in emission.
2. According to Lockyer, H and K lines are the so-called enhanced lines which are produced under high stimulus.
3. Lockyer further asserted that stimulus meant temperature; therefore, the temperature of the chromosphere was *higher* than that of the photosphere.

This last bit was difficult for astrophysicists to swallow and that is why ridicule was poured on Lockyer (but he did not bother one bit). So the question was: What really is going on in the chromosphere? Why does this region emit H and K lines (which occur only at high temperatures), when the chromosphere was expected to be at a lower temperature than the photosphere? This was not all and there were a number of other questions like: Why is that although 92 elements are found on Earth, the Fraunhofer and the flash spectrum of the Sun give no evidence of many elements, e.g., rubidium (Rb) and cesium (Cs)?

To put it in a nutshell, there were many puzzling features about the spectrum of the Sun. And if one extended consideration to the stars, there were even more (apparently) curious phenomena. What were they all due to? Were they all linked and could they be explained on the basis of one single fact? No one knew, but as it turned out there indeed was one single key to all these various puzzles — and that was the Saha ionisation formula. Over now to the next chapter for more about that.

4 *Saha And His Great Discovery*

4.1 Introduction

We come now to Saha's great discovery. In the paper in which he announced the breakthrough, Saha focussed attention on the Sun. But the Sun is a star and what applies to it must apply to other stars as well. So let us quickly see how stellar spectroscopy evolved till Saha entered the picture. [1]

As mentioned before, the foundations for this subject were laid by Fraunhofer and Kirchhoff. The next important landmark is the work of Higgins and Miller who in 1864 reported on the Fraunhofer spectra of about fifty of the brightest stars. They concluded that all the stars they had examined had a chemical composition similar to the Sun. Four years later Secchi outdid Higgins and Miller by publishing a catalogue of nearly 4000 stars. In addition, he arranged them into four groups — white stars like Sirius, yellow stars like the Sun, orange and reddish stars like Betelgeuse and faint red stars. Secchi believed that the colour of the star was an indication of its temperature, white stars being the hottest. Mind you, all this was based purely on visual observations. Photography was then still in its infancy but once it became established, data simply poured in, particularly from the observatory attached to the Harvard University (in America).

By 1920, over two hundred thousand stars had been studied and classified and not surprisingly, the Harvard catalogue was hailed as a great monument of stellar spectroscopy. Like Secchi, the Harvard scientists also arranged the stars in a sequence, being guided in this by the intensity of various spectral lines. For historical reasons, the arrangement order followed the (confusing) alphabetical sequence OBAFGKMNRS. It was generally believed that this was a sequence of decreasing temperature.

---

[1]Some of the concepts in this chapter could be better understood by suitable references to the companion volumes *Why Are Things the Way They Are?* and *Bose and His Statistics*.

4.2 The Chromosphere puzzle

As is to be expected, the spectroscopic study of the Sun was much more thorough and thanks particularly to Lockyer, one knew, among other things, the following:

1. Spectral lines originating in the upper regions of the chromosphere were of the so-called enhanced type.
2. Many elements seen on Earth were not apparent in chromosphere spectra.
3. Helium presented an anomalous case (this anomaly is discussed in detail later).
4. Though heavier, calcium was present at much greater heights in the chromosphere than was hydrogen.

The general feeling was that if one understood what was going on in the Sun, one could figure out what was going on in the stars as well. But in spite of the wealth of data, the Sun remained an enigma. Why? If according to Lockyer the enhanced lines are produced due to higher temperature, then it implied that the top of the chromosphere was at a higher temperature than the photosphere. As Saha remarks in his paper:

> It would lead us to the hypothesis that the outer chromosphere is at a substantially higher temperature than the photosphere and the lower chromosphere; and that the temperature of the Sun *increases* as we pass radially outwards. This hypothesis is, however, quite untenable and is in flagrant contradiction to all accepted theories of physics.

Another problem was the presence of heavier elements at higher altitudes but we shall come to that later. For the moment, let us, like Saha, concentrate on the flash spectrum of the chromosphere and the story it was trying to tell.

Lockyer had said that lines (in the flash spectrum) originating at the top of the chromosphere were similar to those seen in spark spectra. Yes they were, and no argument about that. Lockyer also said that spark lines were "enhanced", the enhancement being due to a stimulus. We can agree on that also. Lockyer now added that temperature was the stimulus and this Saha questioned. Should enhancement come *only* from higher temperature? Is it not conceivable that the temperature was not high but that some other agency was acting as a stimulus? What other agency? To answer this question we must first ask as to what precisely is meant by enhancement. There was the atom, and how did it suddenly become enhanced? Saha realiscd that enhancement meant ionisation (something which Lockyer could not have known about) and that enhanced lines were just lines emitted by an ionised atom. As he declared:

A more plausible explanation is that the lines in question are not due to radiations from the normal atom of the element, but from an "ionised atom, i.e., one which has lost an electron." The high-level chromosphere is, according to this view, the seat of very intense ionisation.

This was a very important and totally new idea, and one which until that time had not been suggested. Qualitatively, many things got immediately explained. Take for example the spectrum of calcium (Ca). The flash spectrum shows three important lines, g due to the normal Ca atom and H and K due to Ca^+ (or CaII); the latter are the so-called enhanced lines. From the curvature of the lines, etc. (recall Fig. 3.14), one could say that normal Ca atoms can be found upto ~ 5000 km, and at greater heights only ionised atoms are present. Many other similar statements could also be made. Of course, one still had to explain why there was preferential ionisation at the upper level, and as we shall soon see that really was Saha's trump card.

4.3 A bit of chemistry

Physics is a quantitative subject and there are not many takers for mere qualitative hand waving. Saha knew that and so he proceeded to outline what he called a theory for the "Ionisation in the Solar Chromosphere"; that in fact was the title of his epoch-making paper.

In his work, Saha was guided by what happens in chemical reactions. More is said about that in the Appendix to this chapter, but to appreciate the basic ideas, consider a closed chamber at a (sufficiently high) temperature T containing the gases CO_2 and H_2. The molecules of CO_2 and H_2 would react according to the equation

$$CO_2 + H_2 \rightarrow CO + H_2O.$$

But gaseous carbon monoxide and water vapour also can react and they do so according to:

$$CO + H_2O \rightarrow CO_2 + H_2.$$

In short, the reaction goes backward and forward like

$$CO_2 \text{ (gas)} + H_2 \text{ (gas)} \rightleftharpoons CO \text{ (gas)} + H_2O \text{ (vapour)}$$

and eventually equilibrium is reached. Under these condition, the number of molecules of CO_2, H_2, CO and H_2O remain constant on the *average*. Note that this does not mean that a given CO_2 molecule will remain as CO_2 forever; it might combine with H_2 and disappear; just that the average number of each species does not change with time, once equilibrium is established.

Now what has all this got to do with the chromosphere? To understand that, we must first appreciate how Saha viewed ionisation. You know that when a solid, e.g., ice, is heated to a proper temperature it melts and becomes a liquid. When the temperature of a liquid is raised sufficiently, it vapourizes. Suppose you keep on heating a monatomic solid. Saha noted that one would then go through the following sequence:

Solid $\rightarrow$ Liquid $\rightarrow$ Gas (atoms) $\rightarrow$ Excited atoms $\rightarrow$ Ionised atoms

     Fusion   Vapourisation   Excitation   Ionisation

You might say: "Hey! Wait a minute. As temperature is increased, eventually the atom becomes ionised. Isn't this what Lockyer also was trying to say, though he used the word enhanced? Then why did Saha come down on him?" That, my dear friend, is precisely where Saha's ingenuity lay.

Let us go back to the example from chemistry. We said that CO_2 and H_2 react to produce the gases CO and H_2O. The amount of CO and H_2O (water vapour) present depends both on the temperature T *as well as* the total pressure P. This was the hint Saha took from chemistry.

When we talk of ionisation in the chromosphere, we should not consider just one atom but a *gas* of atoms. The ionisation proceeds like:

Normal atom $\rightarrow$ Positive ion + Electron.

But the positive ion and the electron could combine, i.e., we could also have the reverse reaction.

Positive ion + Electron $\rightarrow$ Normal atom.

Thus, we have a back and forth affair like:

Normal atom $\rightleftharpoons$ Positive ion + Electron.

In other words, *three* gases are present and are in equilibrium: (i) A gas of normal atoms, (ii) a gas of positive ions and (iii) a gas of electrons. The concentration of ions (or enhanced atoms as Lockyer would call them) will depend on T as well as P. Certainly the concentration of ions would go up if T is raised keeping P fixed. But equally, one might expect the concentration of ions to change if T is fixed and P is varied. What precisely would be the nature of the variation? For this, Saha had to dig further into thermochemistry.

But first let us hear what he has to say about the ionisation idea. He says:

> We may regard the ionisation of a calcium atom as taking place according to the following scheme familiar in physical chemistry,
>
> $$Ca \rightleftharpoons Ca^+ + e - U$$
>
> where Ca is the normal atom of calcium (in the state of vapour), Ca^+ is an atom which has lost one electron, U is the quantity of energy involved in the process. The quantity considered is 1 gm atom.

The next step was to write down a formula connecting x, the fraction of Ca ions, T, P and U. Thanks to his familiarity with thermodynamics, this was no problem at all for Saha. But before we come to the formula itself let us pause and absorb the mood of the times.

The year is 1919. There was the chromosphere with all its puzzles. The Bohr atom model was barely six years old and was not so well known then as it is now. But a few eminent astrophysicists like Jeans and Eddington knew about the Bohr atom, ionisation and all that and Eddington even went so far as to say that deep inside stars, ionised atoms were in equilibrium with radiation. What kind of equilibrium? No one knew.

In 1919, a young man named Eggert in Germany decided to tackle the problem. Eggert was a student of Nernst (see Box 4.1), the man who had discovered the Third Law of Thermodynamics (see *A Hot Story*). Nernst applied his "Heat Theorem" wherever he could (!), including in explaining equilibrium in chemical reactions. It was natural for Eggert to draw inspiration from his teacher and

---

Box 4.1 This is what Saha himself wrote (in *Science and Culture*) in 1942 when Nernst died.

We are very sorry to learn the news of the passing away of Prof. W. Nernst, the great physical chemist of Germany. Nernst's

Theoretical Chemistry was for many years a standard treatise for students of physical chemistry all over the world ...

Professor Nernst was born in 1864 in East Prussia ... A man of extraordinary energy and possessed with an equally virile and active mind, he had also strong likes and dislikes ... He had always some academic quarrel with somebody and like certain eminent scientific persons, the excitement of fighting, which was often harmless, appears to have had a stimulating effect on his intellect ... [He was] behind his rough exterior, a kindly and benevolent soul ...

He was attracted to physical chemistry by William Ostwald and at an unusually early age for Germany, became a professor in the University of Gottingen. Later he was called to occupy the chair of physical chemistry in the University of Berlin, and his laboratory was the nursery of younger physical chemists not only of Germany but of the United States of America, central and eastern countries of Europe, India and Japan. Among his students may be mentioned Langmuir, Lindemann (now Lord Cherwell), Sackur, Simon, Eucken, Plotnikov and many others ... The present writer [Saha] had the good fortune of working at Nernst's laboratory during the summer season of 1921 on an experimental proof of thermal ionisation. He complained to Nernst that compared to the vast activities of the laboratory, it was rather small and wanting in suitable equipments. Nernst gave a characteristic answer: "When you shut a singing bird in a big cage, it refuses to sing."

Nernst will be best remembered by his experimental work on specific heats at low temperatures, his contributions to electrochemistry and his 'Third Law of Thermodynamics' ... Looking over 36 years of Nernst's heat theorem ... one is struck by his great powers of intuition. He rather saw than proved the truth ...

Nernst was very proud of the Third Law, and claimed it as peculiarly his own. "The first and second laws of Thermodynamics", he once remarked, "have been built up by the labours of many men, but the third law is entirely my own."

He has lost two grown up sons in the First World War, and his daughter was married to a banker who was found by the Nazis to have Jewish blood. The consequence was that his grand children could not be German citizens and had to be kept in Oxford in 1936 for their education ...

Einstein was a frequent visitor to Nernst's laboratory in 1921, probably to discuss properties of bodies at low temperature, which might have led later to his theories of gas-degeneration. It was a highly exhilarating sight to see the great propounder of Relativity lounging at leisure on full length in the easy chair, and scarcely uttering a word in minutes, while Nernst would be pacing to and fro, speaking all the time with great animation ...

A Noble prize was awarded to Nernst in 1923.

he sought to develop Eddington's ideas quantitatively. Now in chemistry, whenever there is a reaction there is what is called a *heat of reaction*. If ionisation is viewed as a chemical reaction, then there must be a corresponding reaction energy U. Eggert did not know how to get hold of a value for U. His investigations therefore remained speculative and came to a dead end as it were. Eggert published his work in the German journal *Physikaliche Zeitschrift* and when Saha was casually browsing through that article it suddenly flashed on him that he could do what Eggert had failed to do, i.e., get hold of U. He realised that U could be easily calculated from the ionisation potential and in this way a formula could be had connecting x, the fraction of ionised atoms, T, P and U. Presto, one now had a magic wand. And instead of worrying about stellar interiors as Eggert had done, Saha chose to concentrate on the chromosphere — a wise decision. Saha waved the wand and instantly the chromosphere was obliged to give away its mysteries! Recalling all this years later, Saha said:

It was while pondering over the problems of astrophysics and teaching thermodynamics and spectroscopy to the M.Sc. classes that the theory of thermal ionisation took a definite shape in my mind in 1919. I was a regular reader of German journals which had just started coming after four years of First World War, and in the course of these studies I came across a paper by J. Eggert... in which he applied Nernst's Heat Theorem to explain high ionisation in stars due to high temperatures, postulated by Eddington in the course of his studies on stellar structures.

Eggert, who was a pupil of Nernst and was at that time his assistant, had given a formula for thermal ionisation, but it is rather strange that he missed the significance of the ionisation potential of atoms, the importance of which was apparent from the theoretical work of Bohr and the practical work of Franck and Hertz which was attracting a good deal of attention in those days... Eggert used Sackur's formula of the chemical constant for calculating that of the electron, but in trying to account for multiple ionisation in the interior of stars on this basis he used very artificial values of the ionisation potential.

While reading Eggert's paper I saw at once the importance of introducing the value of the ionisation potential in the formula of Eggert, for calculating accurately the ionisation, single or multiple, of any particular element under any combination of temperature and pressure.

I thus arrived at a formula which now goes by my name [Saha ionisation formula]. Owing to my previous acquaintance with chromospheric and stellar problems, I could at once see its application ...

4.4 Waving the magic wand

This finally brings us to the formula itself or what is now known as the Saha ionisation formula. Applied to a simple reaction like

$$Ca \rightleftharpoons Ca^+ + e\ -U,$$

it reads

$$\log_{10}\left(\frac{x^2}{1-x^2}\right)P = \frac{U}{4.517T} + 2.5\log_{10}T - 6.5. \qquad (4.1)$$

Here x is the fraction of ionised atoms and U is the ionisation energy for one gram atom.

Let us now see how Saha used this formula. If the chromosphere is anything like our atmosphere, one expects both T and P to decrease with height. Possibly P decreased very rapidly, although one did not have a precise idea (then) of how fast the decrease was — see Fig.4.1. Never mind; why not first just see how x varies for various combinations of T and P and then worry about how x varies with height?

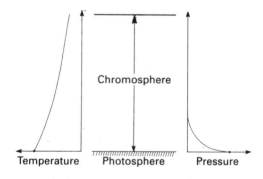

Fig.4.1 Schematic of the variation of T and P with height in the chromosphere, as they were understood in 1919. It was known that both T and P decreased with height, the latter more rapidly than the former. The pressure decrease was known with much less precision than the temperature variation.

Figure 4.2 is a rough schematic of the results obtained by Saha for calcium. The striking fact is that when T is held constant, ionisation increases as pressure decreases. In other words, one expects more ionisation (or enhancement as Lockyer would say) at the top of the

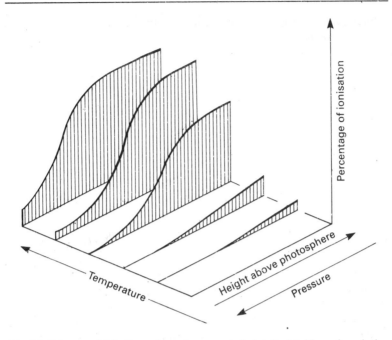

Fig.4.2 Saha used his formula and generated detailed tables of variation of the ionisation fraction x with T and P for various elements. This figure captures the essence of Saha's findings. For a given T, x increases as P decreases (i.e., as height increases). The increase is very strong as T increases. Saha showed that the behaviour of different elements varied because of differences in the ionisation potential. If U is small, then complete ionisation occurs even at moderate heights.

chromosphere than at the bottom. For example, if one takes the temperature at the photosphere as 7500°K and the pressure there as 1 atmosphere (considered a reasonable value), then for calcium, $x = 0.34$, i.e., 34% of calcium atoms would be ionised. Somewhat higher up, one expects T to be lower; say it is $\sim$ 6000°K. If the pressure there is 10^{-4} atmosphere, then $x \sim$ 95%, which implies that at this height practically all the calcium atoms are ionised (even though the temperature has decreased somewhat); and this is what the flash spectrum also indicates — strong g lines from normal calcium atoms at lower levels and H and K lines from Ca^+ at higher levels — see Fig. 4.3.

To you all this might appear simple and straightforward but way back in 1920 it was as if a thick fog had suddenly lifted. Saha did not stop with calcium; he applied his formula to as many elements as he could. For example, he considered barium and strontium which in the periodic table belong to the same group as calcium. There were no surprises, and all facts neatly fitted into place.

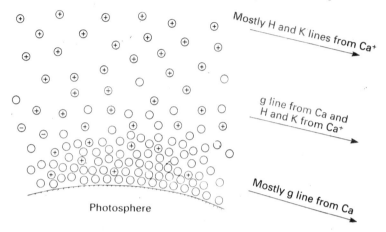

Photosphere

Fig.4.3 The left side of this figure shows schematically how the ratio of normal to ionised atoms of calcium varies with height. Correspondingly, the spectrum originating at higher levels consists predominantly of H and K lines. At lower levels, the g line of normal calcium dominates.

Hydrogen was a bit of a tough customer. Normally, hydrogen is a gas composed of H_2 molecules. Note that in the molecule, two atoms of H are bound together. Now when we talk of ionisation, do we consider the ionised molecule H_2^+ or the ionised atom H^+ (which is nothing but the proton)? By the way, in what form is hydrogen present in the chromosphere? Analysing the problem, Saha came to the conclusion that at temperatures like 6000°K and above, the hydrogen molecule H_2 would dissociate into two separate H atoms. This is to be expected since the energy required to bind two H atoms into a H_2 molecule is rather small, being $\sim$ 3.5 electron volts (eV) per molecule. (This unit of energy is explained in *Why Are Things the Way They Are?*) Thus, at the temperatures prevailing in the chromosphere the atoms in the molecule jingle so violently that the molecule breaks up or dissociates. OK, so the hydrogen in the chromosphere is mostly in the form of atoms rather than molecules. Next question: Is the H atom normal or ionised? The ionisation potential of hydrogen provides the answer. For the H atom it is 13.6 eV, compared to 6.12 eV for calcium. So U is large, and hydrogen barely ionises even at very low pressures such as prevail at the top of the chromosphere. Actually, there is a bit more to the hydrogen story which can be appreciated after reading the next section.

4.5 The case of the missing elements

We are told that 92 elements occur on Earth. If the Earth was born from the Sun (as is generally believed), then all the elements found on Earth must also be found in the Sun. In that case, how come many elements appear to be missing in the Sun? For example, why is it that spectral lines of rubidium (Rb) and Cesium (Cs) are not seen either in the Fraunhofer spectrum or the flash spectrum? This was one of the great puzzles of that time and Saha had an answer for that also. The hint for the answer comes from Table 4.1 which lists a few ionisation potentials.

Table 4.1 Some ionisation potentials

Element	Ionisation potential (eV)
Mg	7.65
Ca	6.12
Sr	5.7
Ba	5.12
Na	5.112
K	4.318
Rb	4.155
Cs	3.873

We see from the table that the ionisation potential is rather low for both Rb and Cs. Thus one would expect both these elements to be completely ionised in the chromosphere at all levels, starting from the bottom. Saha's formula confirms that. Since there are hardly any neutral atoms of Rb and Cs in the chromosphere, one cannot expect any absorption or emission lines associated with neutral atoms. You might not be convinced, but remember that the fact that we fail to see any spectral lines of Rb and Cs does not imply that these elements are actually absent in the Sun. You might still be skeptical. Saha knew people would have such doubts and so he said (effectively): "Look at sunspots and record spectra of those regions of the Sun. In these regions, the temperature is lower. Therefore Rb and Cs would not be 100% ionised and you will definitely see Fraunhofer absorption lines associated with neutral Rb and Cs atoms." Lo and behold! When people looked at sunspots after Saha had made the suggestion, the missing elements Rb and Cs were duly detected. As if this was not enough, Saha asked experimentalists to look also for emission lines of Rb^+ and Cs^+. These occur in the far ultraviolet, a difficult region for experimentation. At that time no data was available but a few years hence when experimental techniques improved, the enhanced lines (as Lockyer would have called them) of Rb and Cs were duly found. So it was confirmed that Rb and Cs were present in the Sun also.

Let us now briefly go back to the concentration of hydrogen ions. What has that got to do with Rb, Cs, Na, etc.? Ah, that is an interesting point.

Remember that x for a particular element in Saha's formula is determined by the values of P and U for that element. Since Na is heavily ionised, and Rb and Cs almost completely so, there is a strong contribution to P from the presence of electrons resulting from the ionisation of the alkali elements. In turn, this influences the ionisation of other elements like H which have a much higher ionisation potential. Therefore, certain species of atoms like Rb and Cs can be very influential in stellar atmospheres, even though their abundance might be much less compared to hydrogen. In other words, we must be careful in using the Saha formula, i.e., we must remember that the partial pressure of the electron gas in the chromosphere has contributions from not just one element but all the elements present. And, even though hydrogen might be more abundant, it contributes less to the electron gas than sodium and rubidium because the latter are more easily ionised.

4.6 The helium mystery

It all reads like a great success story, doesn't it? Indeed it was. Let us now turn to the so-called helium mystery. Briefly, it centred around the following observations:

1. No absorption lines of helium were seen in the Fraunhofer spectrum. (Had they been, helium would have been discovered much before it actually was.)
2. A few lines of helium are seen in the flash spectrum. (This is what lead to the discovery of that element.)
3. The lines associated with the upper regions of the chromosphere, i.e., 7000–8000 km, correspond to normal helium.
4. There is a prominent line at 4686 Å which corresponds to ionised helium. But this originates at $\sim$ 2000 km.

If you think about it, all this is a bit puzzling. How come emission lines are seen but no absorption lines? How come (in contrast to the case of calcium) helium is partially ionised at 2000 km but more or less normal at the much greater height of 8000 km? Saha explained all this quite convincingly.

Four basic facts control the occurrence of absorption as well as emission lines; they apply to helium as also to all other elements. They are:

1. The energy spectrum of the normal atom.
2. The ionisation potential.
3. The relationship of atomic spectral frequencies to the continuous spectrum of radiation emitted by the photosphere.
4. The interplay between T, P and U in Saha's formula which decides the value of x, the fraction of ionised atoms.

Figure 4.4(a) is a simplified and hypothetical energy spectrum of an atom. Some of the possible absorption transitions are shown in Fig.4.4(b). The intensity of the absorption lines depends on two factors, one of which is the population of the individual atomic states. This population distribution depends on the temperature T and how the excited states are positioned with respect to the ground state. When T is small, the upper states would have smaller population compared to the ground state. The second factor which controls the intensity of the absorption lines is the number of photons available

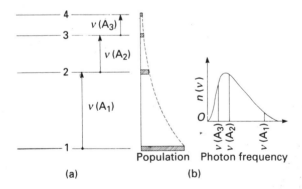

(a)   (b)

Fig.4.4 This figure gives an overview of the issues that control the intensity of Fraunhofer absorption lines. (a) shows a simplistic picture of the energy levels of an atom. In (b) are shown some of the upward transitions which lead to absorption lines. The intensity of the absorption lines is dictated by (i) the population of the initial energy state and (ii) the number of photons in the blackbody spectrum at the corresponding frequencies. These are also shown in (b). Further explanations are given in the text.

in the blackbody spectrum at the absorption frequencies — see Fig.4.4(b). We find that even though the ground state may be highly populated there are not many photons of frequency $\nu(A_1)$ coming from the photosphere to lift the atom to the state 2, producing thereby a dark line at $\nu(A_1)$ in the Fraunhofer spectrum.

Now you might say: "OK, the absorption line at $\nu(A_1)$ is absent but why can't we have lines at frequencies $\nu(A_2)$ and $\nu(A_3)$ in the Fraunhofer spectrum?" Sure, the blackbody spectrum might be more favourable at these frequencies but for the transition A_2 to be visible, there must be a sufficient number of atoms in state 2 to start with. Suppose the population of state 2 is low (this would be so if level 2 is at a rather higher energy). Then we will not see the absorption line $\nu(A_2)$. If $\nu(A_2)$ is not seen, then $\nu(A_3)$ has even slimmer chances of being visible. All this can be made quantitative and in this way one can understand why helium does not contribute dark lines to the Fraunhofer spectrum.

But what about emission lines? What controls them? The answer can be appreciated with the help of Fig.4.5. Unlike the absorption lines, the emission line intensity is not linked to the blackbody spectrum; it is dependent entirely on the population of the upper energy states and is therefore governed solely by the temperature. In helium, the population of the upper states is rather small. If in spite of this the emission lines are still visible, it is thanks entirely to the total solar eclipse. Thus we can understand why it is that lines of the normal helium atom are not visible in absorption but nevertheless seen in emission.

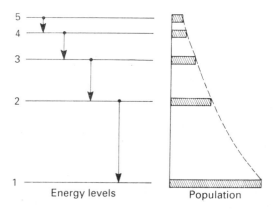

Fig.4.5 This figure is the counterpart of the preceding one and deals with emission lines (such as are found in the flash spectrum). The intensity of the emission line depends entirely on the population n_i of the initial level which in turn depends on T.

What about the curious fact that ionised helium is detected at ~ 2000 km but not at higher levels? This is entirely due to the delicate interplay between x, T, P and U in Saha's formula. The outcome is illustrated in Fig. 4.6 from which we see that unlike in the case of calcium, ionisation of helium, though rather small generally, peaks up slightly at intermediate altitudes. And the emission line of He^+ is found only at intermediate heights.

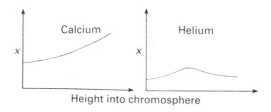

Height into chromosphere

Fig.4.6 Normally, the ionised fraction x increases as one goes up in the chromosphere as in the case of calcium. However, helium is a peculiar case where x peaks at intermediate heights. It is still Saha's formula, but the interplay of parameters is different.

4.7 Selective radiation pressure

One last point before we leave the Sun and move on to the stars. How come a heavier element like Ca is present up to a greater height compared to a light element like H, apparently defying gravity? You will recall that this also was one of the elements of the solar puzzle. Saha had an answer for this one too.

Now the temperature of the photosphere is ~ 7500 °K and the gravitational acceleration there is about 28 times what it is on the surface of the Earth. Both these factors are expected to influence the density variation with height in the chromosphere. Several models to describe this density variation had been proposed and everyone predicted a sharp decrease of density, so much so that one expected hardly any atoms to be present above say 2000 km. For example, a model due to Schwarzchild (a famous theoretical astrophysicist) predicted that at a height of ~ 3500 km, there would be only one atom in a billion cubic metres! However, the flash spectra showed that the abundance of atoms at great heights was much much higher. How were atoms lifted to great heights in defiance of solar gravity? Describing the prevailing opinion, Saha said:

> It seems to be the general opinion of the astrophysicists that there is some sort of a repulsive force on the Sun which neutralizes the greater part of gravity.

But what exactly was this force? In a short paper contributed in 1919 to the *Astrophysical Journal* (published from America), Saha showed that what countered solar gravity was selective radiation pressure. The idea of radiation pressure was by itself not new. It was a natural consequence of Maxwell's electromagnetic theory of light, and laboratory experiments had already been performed to demonstrate the existence of radiation pressure. However, Maxwell's theory also predicted that when the size of the object is reduced the pressure decreases, becoming vanishingly small when the size dwindles to that of an atom. How come then one could think of radiation lifting atoms up into the chromosphere in defiance of solar gravity? Saha had an answer and he said:

An explanation of the existence of radiation-pressure on molecules is furnished when we apply the quantum theory [of Bohr–Sommerfeld; remember in 1919, quantum mechanics was still more than half-a-dozen years away] in place of the old continuous theory of light [i.e., Maxwell's theory].

How exactly does one use the quantum theory? According to Saha, the basic idea is very simple. Following Einstein, one visualizes light energy to be "localized in pulses of energy $h\nu$." Suppose such a pulse is absorbed by an atom of mass M. The light pulse comes with a momentum $(h\nu/c)$ and when it is absorbed this momentum is transferred to the atom, which then moves with a velocity $v = (h\nu/cM)$. If numbers are substituted, the velocity v comes about to be rather small. But, said Saha,

it should be remembered that it [v] is really an impulsive velocity and is of the nature of an acceleration. The total velocity acquired by a hydrogen atom [say] per second will depend upon the number of kicks of light it experiences per second, and provided this is sufficiently great the velocity acquired may rise to enormous values.

Thanks to such velocities, atoms could be carried away to long distances from the chromosphere, creating a thicker blanket of atoms than theories like that of Schwarzchild predicted. Saha adds:

Radiation pressure may exert an effect on the atoms and molecules which is out of all proportion to their actual sizes. It also shows that the radiation pressure exerts a sort of lifting action on the molecules, driving the active ones along the direction of the beam.

Note that an atom will not absorb a light pulse of any arbitrary frequency ν but only a frequency that corresponds to one of the allowed transitions. In this respect the atom is choosy and therefore the pressure experienced by it is called *selective radiation pressure*. Another factor which governs the value of the pressure is how many photons there are at frequency ν in the spectrum coming out of the photosphere. If this number is small, the radiation pressure would correspondingly be low — see Fig. 4.7. In this way we can understand why Ca is present at greater heights compared to H; just that the radiation pressure on Ca is more than that on H.

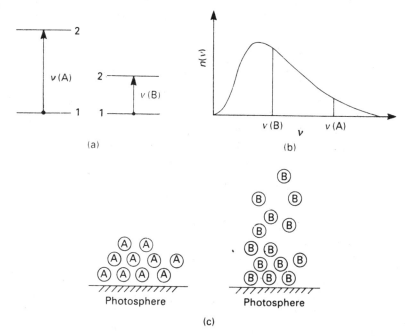

(a) (b)

Photosphere   Photosphere

(c)

Fig.4.7 This figure highlights some considerations relating to selective radiation pressure. (a) shows schematically the absorption lines in two different atomic species. (b) shows the location of these frequencies vis-a-vis the blackbody spectrum. Clearly, there will be less absorption in species A as compared to species B. Therefore, species A will experience less radiation pressure than B. Thus, as shown in (c), atoms of species B would be found at much greater heights in the chromosphere.

In a nutshell, Saha argued that radiation pressure acting on atoms and molecules must not be examined from the classical but the quantum view point. Further, the pressure acting on a particular species of atoms depends very much on (i) what sort of absorption frequencies are available to the atom, and (ii) how intense is the blackbody spectrum at those frequencies. Thus it is that the radiation coming out of the photosphere is able to carry different species of atoms to different heights, i.e., it acts in a *selective* manner. The story of selective radiation pressure does not end here. Saha followed up his short note of 1919 with a much longer paper, but this met with a sad fate. Later Saha recalled:

This [long] paper was sent to the *Astrophysical Journal* for publication but the editors replied that as the paper was rather long, it could be published only if I were willing to bear a part of the printing costs which ran to three figures in dollars. Much as I would have liked to do so, it was not possible for me to find so much money as my salary was rather small and I had to maintain my old parents and a younger brother within this salary. So I wrote to the Editors of the *Astrophysical Journal* expressing my inability to pay the cost of printing, but heard nothing more about the publication of the paper nor was it returned to me. Years afterwards in 1936, when I visited the Yerkes Observatory, Dr. Morgan [the Editor] showed the manuscript which was still being kept there.

Tired of waiting, in 1920 Saha submitted his long paper to a journal published by the Calcutta University. Next year when he was in Europe, he communicated the gist of this long paper to the journal *Nature*. E.A. Milne in England saw this latter note and quickly developed a theory which has since come to be known as Milne's theory of selective radiation pressure. Saha laments:

I might claim to be the originator of the theory of Selective Radiation Pressure ... Milne read a note of mine in *Nature* and in his paper he mentioned my contribution in a footnote, though nobody appears to have noticed it.

Certainly a bit of bad luck there for Saha. As you will read in the next chapter, he had in fact more disappointments. But on the whole, the ionisation formula produced such a terrific impact that it assured him a permanent place in the galaxy of great astrophysicists as it [the formula] not only cleared up many mysteries about the Sun but about stars as well. We pick up that story in the next chapter. But before that, may be it is not a bad idea to summarise what Saha achieved in his epoch-making paper:

- Saha focussed attention on the spectral lines of the Sun, particularly those appearing in the flash spectrum.
- He boldly declared that the enhancement of spectral lines that Lockyer had postulated boiled down to ionisation.

- Next he asserted that ionisation can be produced by heating, and that thermal ionisation can therefore be viewed as a thermochemical reaction.
- Drawing upon his knowledge of thermochemistry, Saha then wrote down a formula relating T, P and x, the fraction of ionised atoms.
- Using his formula along with known values of ionisation potentials for various elements, Saha clearly showed that ionisation in the chromosphere is strongly controlled by the pressure P.
- He was thus able to explain why lines of Na, Rb, Cs, etc., were missing in the Fraunhofer spectrum. He predicted that these elements would be found near sunspots as indeed they later were.
- He was also able to explain various peculiarities such as those associated with H and He.

All this was a mere beginning.

Appendix to Chapter 4

This appendix offers a background to the Saha ionisation formula. Since Saha essentially squeezed it out of thermochemistry, it is useful to start by reminding ourselves of a few basics of chemistry as well as thermodynamics.

Mole, gram molecule, etc.

People in different walks of life often use different counting units. You and I eat one or two bananas at a time but usually we purchase the fruit in units of a dozen. Chemists have a special counting unit when referring to a large number of atoms, all of which belong to the same species (e.g., calcium). This is the *Avogadro number* N_A which is equal to 6.022×10^{23} atoms. Chemists don't use the term Avogadro number; they use instead the word *mole*. To a chemist, mole simply means 6.022×10^{23} atoms. Thus,

$$1 \text{ mole of H atoms} = 6.022 \times 10^{23} \text{ atoms of H,}$$

$$1 \text{ mole of Ca atoms} = 6.022 \times 10^{23} \text{ atoms of Ca, etc.}$$

The term mole is applied to molecules also and hence we have

$$1 \text{ mole of water molecules} = 6.022 \times 10^{23} \text{ molecules of } H_2O.$$

What is the significance of the Avogadro number and why is it important? It represents the number of atoms in X grams of any element, where X denotes the atomic mass of the element concerned. For example, the atomic mass of the element oxygen is 16. Therefore 16 grams of oxygen will contain 6.022×10^{23} atoms of O. To put it differently, 1 mole of any element will weigh X grams, where X is the atomic mass of the element concerned. If we want to know how many atoms there would be in 1 gram, the answer obviously is $(6.022 \times 10^{23}/X)$. This number would naturally vary from element to element; it too has a special name — *gram atom*.

Gases, partial pressure, molefraction, etc.

We next consider a law discovered by John Dalton in 1801. It states:

The total pressure of gas is the sum of the partial pressures of the components of the mixture.

Say we have a mixture of two gases A and B (e.g., oxygen and nitrogen). Dalton's law says:

$$P_{tot} = P_A + P_B , \tag{1}$$

where the notation must be obvious. Recall the P that occurs in Saha's formula; remember that it is the total pressure.

Consider a perfect gas. As you know, its equation of state is:

$$PV = RT.$$

Actually it is implicit here that we have just one mole of the gas. If there are n moles, the formula becomes:

$$PV = nRT.$$

How does one find n? Simple. Let X be the atomic mass or the molecular mass of the species of which the gas is made. For example, for oxygen, $X = 32$ (remember that oxygen gas is made up of O_2 molecules). Let g be the mass of the gas in grams. Then $n = (g/X)$. Thus in the example considered earlier, if n_A and n_B denote the number of moles of the two constituent gases A and B, then from (1) we have

$$n_A \left(\frac{RT}{V} \right) + n_B \left(\frac{RT}{V} \right) = n_{tot} \left(\frac{RT}{V} \right),$$

where

$$n_{tot} = (n_A + n_B).$$

The fraction

$$X_A = \left(\frac{n_A}{n_{tot}} \right)$$

is referred to as the *mole fraction* of A. X_B is defined similarly.

Vapour pressure

Suppose we have a flask as in figure (a). We evacuate it, quickly introduce a small amount of a volatile liquid into it and put the stopper. Some of the liquid will evaporate and soon fill the region above the liquid level. Just as vapourization occurs, condensation too is possible and in equilibrium

liquid ⇌ vapour;

i.e., the rates of forward and backward reactions are the same.

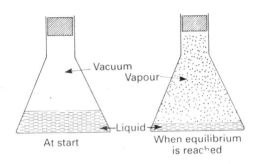

Once equilibrium is reached, the concentration of molecules in the vapour does not change with time. Therefore, the pressure exerted by the vapour on the liquid remains constant. This pressure is called the *vapour pressure*. It is important to note that as long as both the liquid and the vapour are present, the vapour pressure is independent of the volume of the container.

Vapour pressure of solids

The concept of a liquid evaporating and giving rise to a vapour pressure is easy to understand. But do you know that solids too can evaporate? This process is known as *sublimation*. Fortunately it is not very strong but some solids like camphor and naphthalene sublimate (relatively) easily. We can therefore talk of a vapour pressure in this case, and assume that the vapour in equilibrium with a solid behaves like a perfect gas. Books on thermodynamics even derive a formula for it.

If one considers 1 mole of a monatomic solid which undergoes reversible sublimation at temperature T, then its pressure P is given by the following formula:

$$\log_e P = -\frac{l_0}{RT} + \frac{5}{2}\log_e T - \frac{1}{R}\int_0^T dT \left\{ \int_0^T C_p'(T')dT'/T'^2 \right\} + i. \quad (2)$$

Here l_0 is the heat of sublimation at $0°K$ and $C_P(T)$ is the molar specific heat of the solid at constant pressure. Doesn't matter if it sounds a bit technical. I merely want you to notice the following things:

1. We have a formula that looks like Saha's formula, i.e., P depends on T and l_0 (which plays a role like U in Saha's formula).
2. There is a term i standing by itself. This is an important term. It arises due to some integrations during the derivation and for a while, people did not know how to determine it (the constant of integration i).

I would now like to elaborate on this second point. Supposing one tries to derive a formula for the molar entropy of a perfect gas. Classical thermodynamics leads to the result

$$S = C_v \log_e T + R \log_e V + S_0 \qquad (3)$$

where S_0 is a constant of integration. Not surprisingly, the i we had earlier is related to S_0 above (because the formula for P makes use of the formula for S). After Planck discovered the quantum theory, two people named Sackur and Tetrode found out how to calculate the "missing link" S_0. And they showed that

$$S = C_v \log_e T + R \log_e V + R \log_e \left\{ \frac{(2\pi m k_B)^{3/2}}{h^3 N_A} \right\} + \frac{5}{2} \qquad (4)$$

where m is the atomic mass of the element making up the solid, h is Planck's constant and N_A is Avogadro's number. If you compare this with the earlier formula (3), you can easily see what the value of S_0 is. Further analysis shows that the constant of integration i in (2) is given by

$$i = \log_e \left\{ \frac{(2\pi m)^{3/2} (k_B)^{5/2}}{h^3} \right\}. \qquad (5)$$

With this value for i, we have a complete formula for the vapour pressure P of sublimation.

A small digression here. Notice that all logarithms in (2) are to the natural base e. These days everyone uses calculators and computers but in the old days we had to use "log tables" which gave the logarithm of various numbers to the base 10. $\log_e x$ is related to $\log_{10} x$ by:

$$\log_{10} x = \left(\frac{\log_e x}{2.30} \right).$$

So if we write formula (2) in terms of logarithms to the base 10, we would have

$$\log_{10} P = -\frac{l_o}{2.30RT} + \frac{5}{2}\log_{10} T - \frac{1}{2.30R}$$

$$\times \int_o^T \left\{ \int_o^T C_p(T')dT'/T'^2 \right\} dT \qquad (6)$$

$$+ R\log_{10} \left\{ \frac{(2\pi m)^{3/2}(k_B)^{5/2}}{h^3} \right\}.$$

Some books (e.g., *Heat and Thermodynamics* by Sears and Zemansky) adopt the following conventions:

$\log_e x$: write as $\ln x$

$\log_{10} \sim$: write as $\log x$.

In other words, depending on whether you have $\log x$ or $\ln x$, the base is 10 or e.

Law of mass action

Consider now the reaction

$$CO_2 + H_2 \rightleftharpoons CO + H_2O$$

discussed in section 4.3. As a generalisation, let us consider four substances A_1, A_2, A_3 and A_4 which react under equilibrium according to:

$$\nu_1 A_1 + \nu_2 A_2 \rightleftharpoons \nu_3 A_3 + \nu_4 A_4. \qquad (7)$$

We have, for convenience, restricted only to four constituents. The ν's are called *stoichiometric* coefficients; they are always positive and can be either integers or fractions, e.g., in the reaction

$$H_2O \rightleftharpoons H_2 + \frac{1}{2} O_2 \text{ (you might prefer } 2H_2O \rightleftharpoons 2H_2 + O_2),$$

the ν' s are : 1, 1, 1/2. Let us say that equilibrium has been attained in the reaction (7) and let x_1, x_2, x_3, x_4 be the equilibrium mole fractions of the four species.

In the last century it was discovered that in reactions like the above, one quantity remains constant. Denoted K and called the *equilibrium constant*, it is defined as

$$K = \left(\frac{x_3^{\nu_3} x_4^{\nu_4}}{x_1^{\nu_1} x_2^{\nu_2}} \right) p^{(\nu_3 + \nu_4 - \nu_1 - \nu_2)}. \tag{8}$$

K has the dimensions of pressure raised to the power $(\nu_3 + \nu_4 - \nu_1 - \nu_2)$. This constancy of K is also sometimes referred to as the *law of mass action*. Books on chemistry are full of details about this law, how useful K is, etc. Perhaps you are not able to see what is so great about K. Maybe the data given below would help.

Let us go back to the reaction

$$CO_2 + H_2 \rightleftharpoons CO + H_2O.$$

Here all the stoichiometric coefficients are unity. Careful experiments at $1259°K$ resulted in the following data. In every case, the reaction was started off with certain fractions of CO_2 and H_2. When equilibrium was attained, the individual x_k's were measured and the value of K was computed. As you can see, the K value remains the same.

Starting mixture		Equilibrium mixture			
x_{CO_2}	x_{H_2}	x_{CO_2}	$x_{CO} = x_{H_2O}$	x_{H_2}	K
0.101	0.899	0.0069	0.094	0.805	1.60
0.491	0.509	0.2122	0.2790	0.2295	1.60
0.609	0.391	0.3443	0.2645	0.1267	1.60
0.703	0.297	0.4750	0.2282	0.0685	1.60

What has all this got to do with the Saha ionisation formula? It goes back to Nernst who wanted to know how to calculate K. You will recall that K is pressure raised to some power; so, $\log K$ must have a formula rather like (6). Indeed, and the formula derived by Nernst has the form

$$\log_e K = -\frac{\Delta H_0}{RT} + \frac{1}{R} \int \left\{ \int \frac{\Sigma C_p dT}{T^2} \right\} dT + \frac{\Sigma S_0}{R}. \tag{9}$$

I shall not go into the details of this formula; instead I shall just draw your attention to the following:

1. ΔH_0 is the heat of reaction at $0°K$. Eggert tried to use (9) for

describing the interior of stars where, according to Eddington, electrons and ions of various species were in equilibrium. But Eggert did not know how to estimate ΔH_0.

2. The quantity ΣS_0 represents a sum of S_0 for all the species, S_0 having the same meaning as in (3). Thanks to Sackur and Tetrode, one knew how to obtain this term. As Saha has remarked, Nernst insisted on taking proper account of this term.

As a result of his careful study of thermodynamics, Saha was aware of all this. At the same time, he had kept up with atomic physics and quantum theory (such as it existed in those days), and in addition he also knew all about the chromosphere problem. So, when Eggert's paper appeared, he saw a great opportunity to skilfully combine these bits and pieces. He first picked up Nernst's formula and tuned it to his situation. This gave him formula (4.1). Next he used values of the ionisation potential to calculate U for various elements. After this it was the home stretch; all he had to do was to explain the various observed results.

In retrospect, one must also say that Saha was rather lucky in that he was able to get there first. Later it became known that Lindemann in England and Kramers in Holland were also attacking the problem of ionisation in stellar atmosphere. It was indeed very very creditable for Saha to have accomplished so much working in far away Calcutta, practically in isolation, with hardly anyone to discuss or consult. Sometimes, adverse circumstances bring out the best in a person.

5 *From The Sun To The Stars*

5.1 Westward ho!

In Chapter 1 we saw Saha as a young lecturer at Calcutta University, trying not only to make a mark as a good teacher but also as a researcher. Saha published his first paper in 1917 and quickly followed it up with several more in the next couple of years. The topics varied and there was no central theme as such, although the electron and radiation received preferential attention. Be that as it may, they were substantial enough for the Calcutta University to award him the D.Sc. degree in 1918. In between Saha got married.

And then in 1919, there appeared the paper by Eggert (to which a reference has already been made). As if on cue, Saha burst forth with a flood of papers on ionisation, solar and stellar spectra, radiation pressure and all that. Mind you, Saha was then working in complete isolation — no guide or expert around to whom he could turn for advice or criticism.

A change now came over Saha. He was eager to go to Europe, visit labs, mingle with peers, exchange ideas and accelerate his research. But travel requires money and Saha had none. So he had to compete for studentships and fellowships. Among other things, the competition required him to submit a technical essay under an assumed name (nom de plume, as the French call it) and Saha wrote one entitled, *On the Harvard Classification of Stellar Spectra.* Saha's essay was so much superior to the other entries that both the Premchand Roychand Studentship and the Guru Prasanna Ghosh Fellowship easily came to him. With some guarantee of money in the pocket, Saha set sail for Europe in September 1919.

5.2 European sojourn

After arriving in London, Saha discovered that his coveted studentship and fellowship did not really provide him with enough money. Something had to be done quickly both on the financial side and the scientific as well. Fortunately he ran into an ex-classmate who was then at the Imperial College of Science and Technology, London. This friend said, "Why don't you call on Prof. A. Fowler in our Institute? He was earlier an assistant to Sir Norman Lockyer, and is a famous stellar astrophysicist. Maybe he can help you." Saha took the advice and immediately sought an interview with Prof. A. Fowler, which was granted. When they met, Saha showed Fowler his prize-winning essay and Fowler was duly impressed. He then permitted Saha to work in his lab and also took upon himself to advise Saha. Under Fowler's guidance Saha rewrote his essay, giving it a new title: *On a Physical Theory of Stellar Spectra.* Fowler communicated this paper to the Royal Society which promptly published it in its Proceedings; as expected, the paper attracted wide attention, especially in America. Recalling this later Saha said:

> I took about four months in rewriting this paper, and all the time I had the advantage of Professor Fowler's criticism, and access to his unrivalled stock of knowledge of spectroscopy and astrophysics. Though the main ideas and working of the paper remained unchanged, the substance matter was greatly improved on account of Fowler's kindness in placing at my disposal fresh data, and offering criticism whenever I went a little astray out of mere enthusiasm.

Commenting on the relationship between the Indian visitor and his English patron, astronomer Dingle once observed:

> On thinking back to the relation which existed between Saha and Fowler, I am tempted to compare it with that between Maxwell and Faraday.

London was truly a far cry from Calcutta, not merely in terms of geographical distance; not only the cultural milieu but the whole working style was different. Saha made many friends, including of Indians there who had come for study or work or both. Prominent among these was S.S. Bhatnagar, later to make a monumental contribution by founding the CSIR chain of laboratories. Bhatnagar was such a lively go-getter that Saha used to refer to him as Steam Ship Bhatnagar!

Fowler's lab was a welcome change from Calcutta University, for here Saha could meet many experts and get all the latest news from Europe very quickly. Arnold Sommerfeld in Germany was revolutionising the theory of atomic spectra, and Saha had the wonderful chance to keep up with the rapid developments. Alongside, he was also keen to do experiments to verify his theory of thermal ionisation. This called for high-temperature facilities which, however, were not available in England. But they were in Nernst's lab in

Berlin, and on Fowler's advice Saha wrote to Nernst who promptly extended an invitation to visit and do the experiments. The year was 1920, and Germany was still smarting under the defeat she had suffered at the hands of England during the First World War. So Nernst flatly refused permission to British and American scientists when they wrote to him expressing a desire to visit his lab. But in Saha's case he made an exception because he was an Indian!

Saha spent a year in Nernst's lab and the German visit proved an immense boon. Right next to the lab was where the University Colloquium was held every week and Saha never missed any. As a result he was able to see and even meet many eminent German physicists like Max Planck, von Laue and Einstein. Meanwhile, Saha sent a copy of his paper on stellar spectra to Sommerfeld who at once invited him to Munich to deliver a Seminar. Saha's visit to Munich coincided with that of Rabindranath Tagore. Saha did not know the poet but Sommerfeld did and he arranged an introduction. On the following day Saha called on Tagore who received him very affectionately, enquired about his work, and invited him to visit Shantiniketan on his return to India. Till the end, Saha always had a great regard for Tagore, almost amounting to worship (see Box 5.1).

Sommerfeld also took a great liking for Saha and years later when he visited India it was Saha who planned the trip for him. Sommerfeld had a wonderful visit, especially in Calcutta (where he met Raman and Tagore) and in Madras (where he inspired young Chandrasekhar — see *Chandrasekhar and His Limit*).

Box 5.1 This is what Saha wrote on the occasion of the seventieth birthday of Tagore.

Our Rabindranath, in our beautiful mother-tongue, has always sung of the True, the Good and the Beautiful. In the course of his long life (may it be longer still), the surging events of the times have always found a ready response in his poetical heart. Sometimes like Homer, he sings in irresistible strains of the prowess of an old hero, then he passes into a deeper mood, and sings of piety and devotion like an old Hebrew prophet. Sometimes like Aeschylus he repaints an old story in more gorgeous colours of morality and virtue; and again, like Aristophanes, he pours scorn on the still lingering old-world superstitions with simply crushing effect. Sometimes like the old master Kalidasa, he picks up words like a jeweller, and pieces them together with the finest effect, then he relapses into the simple unaffected art of the country poet. His career reads like a poetical Odyssey, and he is the old, yet the ever young poet. In him the art of speech has reached its perfection.

From Germany Saha went to Switzerland and then back to England where he met the great Eddington at Cambridge. Eddington invited Saha to his house and there he was introduced to Milne who was then Eddington's assistant. Milne told Saha that he had seen his (Saha's) paper on radiation pressure in *Nature* and that he had done further work on the subject. Milne added that he was collaborating with R.H. Fowler (not to be confused with A. Fowler! see Box 5.2) on extending Saha's work.

Box 5.2 The name of Ralph Howard Fowler has been mentioned several times in this series of books; so perhaps it is worthwhile including some biographical notes about him. R.H. Fowler was born in England in 1889. In school he distinguished himself both in classics (i.e., Greek and Latin) as also mathematics, but in college, it was in mathematics that he specialized. He studied in Trinity College, Cambridge and did so well that he bagged the Rayleigh Prize. After obtaining the MA degree, he plunged into pure mathematics. He was attracted to differential equations — the Emden equation in particular (see the companion volume *Chandrasekhar and His Limit*). This inevitably brought him into contact with astrophysicists, for the solutions that he discovered helped in understanding and classifying possible stellar configurations. Fowler's biographer records that his paper on this subject "is a typical example of Fowler's merciless search for complete generality which was always characteristic of him." An interesting observation this, for it applies even more to Fowler's "student" Chandrasekhar.

At this stage of Fowler's career the First World War broke out and like many other scientists of the day, Fowler was called to active duty. He was not posted to the front but asked to help the munition department. Here he came into contact with A.V. Hill (whose name will appear later), and together they invented an optical instrument that could track aeroplanes in flight. As it turned out, the instrument was used more to study ballistic projectiles and served to verify a theory developed by the mathematician Littlewood.

After the War Fowler returned to Cambridge where he now switched to mathematical physics. His first work of importance was a method (developed along with Charles Darwin, the grandson of the great explorer and author of the *Origin of Species*) for rigourously calculating the partition function. Meanwhile the ionization problem caught his fancy and his contributions in this area are described in the text. In 1926, Fowler published the most original paper of his lifetime, i.e., the theory of the white dwarf. You can learn more about it in the companion volume *Chandrasekhar and His Limit*.

Fowler became a very good friend of Lord Rutherford despite their strongly contrasting personalities. Whereas Fowler's approach to physics was highly mathematical, Rutherford was always impatient with abstract mathematical theory. But Rutherford's robust and rugged genius

appealed to Fowler, and Fowler's amazing versatility impressed Rutherford. Eventually Fowler married Rutherford's only daughter.
Fowler was an excellent golfer and a "fierce" cricketer who "bowled
fast and often erratically!" In 1935, Fowler succeeded Sir William Bragg
as the Director of the National Physical Laboratory. He died in 1944.

Saha realised more than ever before that his formula really held
the key to the stars. He desperately needed spectroscopic data but
alas there was very little of it in either England or continental
Europe. However, there were tons of it in America and so why not
knock on that door?

5.3 No invitation to the party

The premier observatory in America at that time was the Mount
Wilson Observatory, and the man in charge of it was George Ellery
Hale. Mount Wilson boasted of the world's largest telescope and
the data they did not have was not worth having. Saha wrote to
Hale pleading for data but there was no reply. But that did not
mean that Saha was totally ignored — the man Saha was ignored
but not his theory!

Henry Norris Russell of Princeton University (see Box 5.3) was
one of those who took quick and serious notice of Saha's work.
In fact Russell realised that this was the master key to stellar
spectra he was looking for all along. Meanwhile Saha's papers kept
appearing in quick succession and Russell felt he should move fast.
To his friend Walter Adams in Mount Wilson he wrote:

I believe that within a few years we may utilize knowledge of ionisation potentials, and so on, to obtain numerical determination of
stellar temperatures from spectroscopic data.

Box 5.3 Henry Norris Russell was born in 1877 in New York State
(America). From his mother, Eliza Norris, he inherited a flair for
mathematics and puzzle solving, and also a keen sense of duty. His
parents sent him to live with his aunt in Princeton as there were good
schools there. Blessed with a photographic memory, Russell breezed
through school and at the age of 16 entered the Princeton University to
study Mathematics and Astronomy. There he came under the influence
of C.A. Young (he has been mentioned earlier), a pioneer in solar
spectroscopy. For his Master's degree, Russell did a thesis on the visual
classification of stellar spectra. For his Ph.D., he studied the perturbation
of the orbit of Mars, due to the newly discovered asteroid Eros. Later
this became his style — blending mathematics with experimental data.

Russell got his doctorate in 1900 and fell ill soon after. To recover, he went on a holiday to France. Back in health he then went to Cambridge University in England to do post doctoral work. He returned to America in 1905, took up a faculty position in Princeton University and plunged heavily into research. His first major problem was to find some kind of an order amongst stars in relation to their various characteristics, and the outcome was the famous Hertzsprung–Russell (H–R) diagram. While engaged in this work, Russell needed a lot of astronomical data and for this he turned to Pickering, the then Director of Harvard Observatory.

In 1910, Russell became a Full Professor. During World War I his attention turned to a few applied problems, but once the war was over, he came back to research in astrophysics. He realised that whereas America led Europe in observational astronomy, it was the other way around in theoretical astrophysics. He therefore strongly urged American scientists not to remain content with merely accumulating observational data — that was rather like stamp collecting. Thus, commenting on the work of one Miss Cannon at the Harvard Observatory, Russell wrote to Pickering:

> To be quite frank it seems to me that Miss Cannon has been more concerned with what the spectra *look like* than what they *mean*. I do not think this fact diminishes the service she has rendered to astronomy; on the contrary, her strict attention to facts disregarding the current theories, has given her a peculiar aptitude for her great work.

It was just around this time that Saha's flood of papers appeared and this was just the handle that Russell was looking for. Along the line arose the great controversy about hydrogen. According to theoretical astrophysicists, hydrogen was only a minor constituent element in the stars, other elements, e.g. iron, being more dominant. On the other hand, spectroscopic evidence suggested that hydrogen dominated all stellar atmospheres. Most theorists including Russell were not inclined to accept this evidence, their belief being that the experiments were not quite OK. For a while Russell clung tenaciously to the idea that hydrogen was unimportant but when the experimental evidence proved overwhelming, he became one of the strongest supporters of the hydrogen case. In a long paper published in 1929, he firmly declared that stellar atmospheres were, after all, mostly hydrogen.

Meanwhile the quantum revolution had broken out and atomic spectroscopy received a tremendous shot in the arm because systematic methods now became available to deal with complex spectra. Correspondingly, by using this new knowledge, one could have a better understanding of stellar atmosphere. Once again all the action on the theoretical front was in Europe and this left Russell uncomfortable. To add to this problem, the new quantum mechanics seemed a mystery. However, thanks to his keen skills in puzzle solving he managed to survive professionally. In fact in atomic spectroscopy there is a model known as Russell–Saunders coupling which describes one way of combining the orbital and spin angular momenta of the electrons in the atom.

Russell died in 1957.

A few months later Russell went to California and discussing Saha's work in a seminar said:

Astronomy, physics and chemistry now had an atomic model for the emission and absorption of radiation ...

After pointing out how Saha's formula had solved many of the riddles of the chromosphere, Russell added:

This is but a single illustration of the immense possibilities of the new field of investigation which opens up before us. A vast deal of work must be done before it is even prospected — much less worked out, and the astronomer, the physicist, and the chemist must combine in the attack ... It is not too bold to hope that, within a few years, science may find itself in possession of a rational theory of stellar spectra, and, at the same time, of much additional knowledge concerning the constitution of atoms.

Russell knew exactly what was to be done and where to tap for data — Mount Wilson. He wanted astronomers, physicists and chemists to work together. Fine. Meanwhile, there was Saha the man who got the ball rolling. Would it not be the obvious thing to ask him to join this collaborative endeavour? No. Commenting on all this, the American scientific historian de Vorkin later wrote:

Many others based their own work on Saha's but it was at Mount Wilson, under the coordination of Russell and Hale's staff, that the general attack on spectra took place. As a favour to Hale, Russell answered Saha's letter, outlining the planned agenda for Mount Wilson. He assured Saha that they were going to follow his lead. Saha, however, was not invited to the party.

5.4 Reconstructing the life history of a star

From the purely narrative, let us turn to the scientific part of the history to see how Saha's papers spurred further development. For this a digression is first needed and we must ask: What are the basic questions that confront the astronomer? Saha himself has listed them for us and they are the following:

1. How do stars come into existence and what is their life history?

2. How do they maintain their stock of energy?
3. What happens to the radiation which is being poured out into space?
4. What is the ultimate fate of the Universe?

Perhaps you might like to add a few more to the list, but in Saha's time at least, these were the basic questions. Of course, we shall briefly consider only the first.

As you know, stars live for billions of years whereas a human being lives at most for say a hundred years. Even if we take the accumulated experience of all humanity, it barely adds up to a few thousand years. How then are we to reconstruct the life history of a star? Good question, and Saha has answered it by quoting the astronomer Sir John Hershel who says:

> Suppose an intelligent observer who has never seen a tree is allowed one hour's walk in a forest. During this time, he will not see a single leaf unfold; yet he could find sprouting seeds, small saplings, young, full-grown, and decrepit trees, and fallen trunks mouldering into earth, and in that brief hour he might form a correct idea of the life-history of a tree.

As Saha remarks, what the astronomer does is exactly parallel. Using his telescope and spectroscope he observes as many stars as possible. Each star is in a particular stage of its evolutionary history. By compiling the characteristics of the different stars and observing patterns, he then forms a conceivable picture of stellar evolution.

The situation that existed in 1920 when Saha's papers appeared was roughly as follows:

1. According to Eddington (and a few others as well), a star starts its life as a great big blob of cold gas. As time passes the cloud shrinks, and at the same time becomes hotter. The shrinkage continues but much later the star starts cooling down instead of becoming hotter still. Thus, twice in its lifetime a star will have the same surface temperature, first when it is a giant and later when it is a dwarf — see Fig. 5.1. This evolutionary hypothesis was first put forward by Lockyer, though in a somewhat rudimentary form. Subsequently Russell amplified it and still later Eddington built upon it.
2. As already mentioned, the Harvard Observatory had accumulated mountains of data and Russell was always concerned as to what it all meant. Between 1908 and 1913 he applied his mind vigorously

to the problem and came to the conclusion that the data could be comprehensively represented as a map as shown in Fig. 5.2. Such a plot was independently proposed by Hertzsprung of Denmark and so it is often called the H–R plot (for more about it see *Chandrasekhar and His Limit*. See also Box 5.4). In this plot, the x-axis is not a physical parameter but a sequence of alphabets introduced by the Harvard scientists Pickering and Cannon. And yet when Russell made the plot or map, he found that most known stars clustered in a band. How could that be unless the alphabets were in some (mysterious) way related to some physical parameter of the star? Pickering and Cannon proposed a sequence because they observed that the spectra changed continuously across the sequence. But what really caused this change? No one knew for sure. Russell suspected that it was the temperature (of the stellar atmosphere) that caused the change but he could not explain how temperature variation caused a gradual change in the absorption spectra.

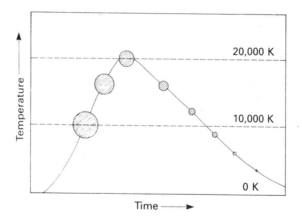

Fig.5.1 Schematic of the temperature variation of a star during its lifecycle. The circles represent the size. Observe that the star starts as a giant and ends as a dwarf (which happens when the nuclear fuel is all burnt). Also notice that twice during its life, the star has the same surface temperature.

Box 5.4 As I have mentioned in the text, the H–R diagram has been discussed in the companion volume on Chandra. Even so, it is worthwhile to add a few remarks here, especially about the so-called Harvard scale.

People have been observing stars for ages and right from those days, they always referred to bright stars as well as faint stars. So brightness was perhaps the first parameter used for classifying stars. Later, after the invention of the telescope, people could see that stars had some slight colour ranging from dull red to bright white. This was immediately related to what happens, for example, when a piece of iron is heated in a big fire. First it becomes hot, then it turns dull red and eventually glows bright white. Thus when Secchi grouped stars according to their colour, he knew that colour really meant temperature. If one could measure the colour of the star, and had a calibration curve relating colour and temperature, then one had a way of determining the temperature of the star. Many people including Russell did attempt such a colour to temperature conversion but it was far from satisfactory.

Meanwhile, telescopes improved, photographic recording improved, and spectroscopes also improved. High quality data began to accumulate, particularly from the Harvard Observatory. Pickering and Miss Cannon who were churning out the data then said: "Spectral data is very good and precise. Why don't we group and classify stars according to their spectra?"

How does one go about this business? Not too difficult if you think about it a bit. Now there are spectral lines and spectral lines. Some belong to the same element, some belong to the ionised element (the so-called enhanced lines) and still others belong to different elements. Not all lines appear in all spectra. Therefore one may, to start with, group stars which have rather similar spectra. When this sort of preliminary sorting was done, Pickering and Cannon found that there were just a handful of groups. Next they asked: "Is there any way in which these seven or eight groups can be arranged as a sequence?" It turned out this was possible because the spectrum found in one group appears to be 'gradually transforming' into the spectrum in another group. What I mean is roughly the following. Say there are two elements M_1 and M_2. In one group of stars, the lines of M_1 are prominent and those of M_2 are weak; in another group it is the other way around. It is then reasonable to regard these as two "neighbouring" groups. In this way Pickering and Cannon arranged the groups and obtained a sequence. For historical reasons the alphabets O, B, A, F, G, K, M, N were attached to the members of this sequence.

Next came some detailing. Take a group like A. In this 'basket' there are many stars; any way of sequencing them? Yes there was, by focussing on one prominent line of one element and seeing how its intensity varied amongst the members of the 'basket'. There were other tricks too. The net result was there was now a lot of fine structure. One no longer talked of just B, but of subgroups with labels like B_0, B_5, B_8, etc. In short, Pickering and Cannon invented a systematic way of arranging the 20,000 odd stars for which data had painstakingly been collected. The sequencing was logical, and clearly there was some parameter that was responsible for the gradual variation of the spectra. One suspected it was the temperature but one had at that time no way of relating the appearance of stellar spectra to the temperature (and the pressure) of the stellar atmosphere. That there was something hiding behind the Harvard sequence became more forcefully evident when Russell made the H–R plot. Why should stars cluster in a band unless the sequence O B A F ... had some meaning? What meaning? Temperature? How does temperature affect spectra of stars? Dead end there!

Astronomers were stuck like this for nearly thirty years or so till Saha's paper appeared. Therefore to many, Russell included, it was like the Sun breaking through the clouds.

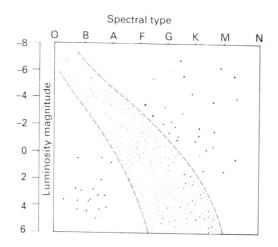

Fig.5.2 This is a schematic of the H–R diagram (which figures prominently also in the volume on Chandra). Basically, it is a map in which stars are assigned a place dependent on their luminosity (*y*-scale) and type (*x*-scale). Here the type is not based on a physical parameter but an apparently arbitrary sequence of alphabets. What is remarkable is that despite this seemingly arbitrary type casting, the stars cluster together in a band. Russell recognized this to be significant, particularly in relation to the evolution theory of stars. The question was: What really does the *x*-axis represent? Russell believed it was temperature, but how to convert the alphabet sequence into a temperature scale? The answer is given in the text.

And then in December 1920, Saha's first paper on thermal ioni- sation appeared. Immediately Russell caught on to its significance because here was the clue he was all along desperately searching for. In July 1921 Russell wrote a short article for *Scientific American* entitled *What a Study of Atoms and Electrons Tells Us of the Stars*, and in it he drew the attention of his readers to Saha's discovery.

He said:

> Many beautiful applications of this theory have recently been worked
> out by an Indian physicist Dr. Megh Nad Saha, of the University of
> Calcutta. Much of the foregoing discussion is adapted from his work,
> and one more instance of it may be given. The dark lines of sodium
> are strong in the solar spectrum. Those of potassium are present
> but weak. The rare alkali metals, rubidium and caesium show many
> strong lines but these do not appear in the sun at all. This has long
> been a puzzle, but Dr. Saha has given the solution.

Russell (prophetically) adds:

> When more laboratory work has been done on these matters, it
> probably will be possible to calculate with fair precision the temper-
> atures of the atmosphere of the various types of stars, simply from
> a knowledge of the degree to which the various sorts of atoms in
> them are ionised, as indicated by the lines in their spectra.

5.5 Saha and the stars

Russell was not aware at that time that Saha had already taken
the first step in this direction in his prize-winning essay. As I
mentioned earlier, in England Saha polished this essay (under A.
Fowler's guidance) and submitted it to the *Proceedings of the Royal
Society*. Let us now briefly see what Saha achieved in that paper.
Saha begins by quoting Russell who says:

> The spectra of the stars show remarkably few radical differences in
> type. More than 99% of them fall into one or the other of the six
> great groups which during the classic work of the Harvard College
> Observatory ... received designations ... by the rather arbitrary letters
> B A F G K M. That there should be so few types is noteworthy,
> but much more remarkable is the fact that they form a continuous
> series.

Saha then continues:

> Russell is of the opinion that the principal differences in the stellar
> spectra arise in the main from variations in a single physical variable
> in the stellar atmosphere ...

What could that variable be? Everything pointed to temperature.
Russell had already guessed it was the temperature but did not know
how to get at it precisely.

It is necessary at this stage to understand how the intensity of Fraunhofer lines would be affected by temperature. For this, let us first consider what happens when an assembly of neutral atoms is progressively heated. The population of the various states would then vary as schematically shown in Fig.5.3. Suppose we consider a particular state of quantum number n. Unless $n = 1$ and the atom is also neutral, the population of that state would first increase and then decrease, affecting thus the intensity of the absorption line originating from it — see Fig.5.4.

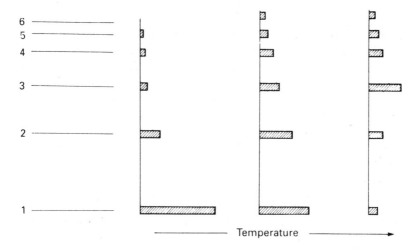

Fig.5.3 This figure illustrates schematically how temperature affects the population of the various levels of a neutral atom. On the left is shown a set of energy levels. The horizontal bars on the right indicate the population of the various levels at different temperatures.

If the heating is progressively continued, above a certain temperature T all the atoms would be ionised. The story would now repeat for the spectral lines of the singly ionised species of atoms; at a still later stage the ions would all become doubly ionised and their lines would follow the same behaviour, and so on. In short, if we consider a particular absorption line and study its intensity as a function of temperature, we may expect something like that in Fig.5.4.

How to be sure that all this is true, logical though it seems? Obviously, experimental data must be the arbiter. Saha even visualised how the experiment ought to be done, what one would see, etc., but where actual data was concerned there was none. So, in order to test his hypothesis, Saha turned to the stars.

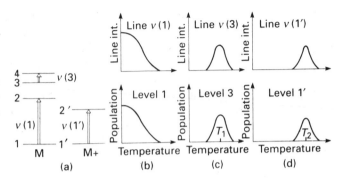

Fig.5.4 (a) shows simplified level schemes of the neutral and the ionised atoms and some transitions leading to absorption lines. (b), (c), (d) show schematically the temperature variations of the populations of various levels and the intensities of the related absorption lines. Level 1 is heavily populated at low temperatures. Thus the intensity of $\nu(1)$ shows merely a decline as level 1 gets progressively depleted. In the case of level 3, the population goes through a peak and correspondingly also the line intensity. In the case of M^+, level $1'$ is initially not populated. Hence in this case also one sees a peaking. Notice that the peak in M^+ occurs at a much higher temperature, i.e., $T_2 > T_1$.

What did stellar data show? Consider a particular Fraunhofer line of a particular element, say the K line of Ca^+. If the intensity of this line as revealed in the data for stars of various types is examined, then it is found to have a variation roughly as in Fig. 5.5. This intensity is a measure of the extent to which calcium is ionised in a particular type of star. If one takes the pressure in the atmosphere of all stars to be the same (i.e., at the "ground" or the photosphere level of the star concerned) and to be in the region 1–0.1 atmospheres, then one can estimate T for the star and in this way Saha arrived at tentative values as in Fig.5.5.

Summarising, Saha showed:

- That his analysis corroborated Russell's view that continuous variation of stellar spectra among the various types was due to the variation of a single parameter.
- That the parameter in question was temperature.
- That he could convert the arbitrary Harvard scale of alphabets into a temperature scale based on spectral information.

To put it differently, his theory struck a blow to the idea of protoelements evolving even as stars evolved through their life cycle (you will remember that this is what Lockyer had proposed).

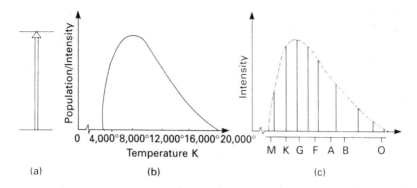

Fig.5.5 This figure summarises how Saha converted the Harvard scale into a temperature scale. (a) shows the transition associated with the K-absorption line of Ca^+. The population of the lowest level varies with temperature as in (b). This is also how the intensity of the K (absorption) line varies across the Harvard sequence . Notice that because we are dealing with an ionised atom, the intensity goes through a peak. This is because initially there are no ionised atoms. (Recall Fig.5.4.) (c) shows (schematically) the variation of intensity of the K line observed across the Harvard sequence. Noting that the intensity disappears at O, Saha fixed the temperature of these types of stars as 20,000°K and this gave him the required conversion.

5.6 Enter Russell

Russell entered the game even as Saha was trying to clear up the mystery of the stars. Whereas Saha had already moved from the Sun onto the stars, Russell chose for a start to go back to the Sun. In a paper entitled *The Theory of Ionisation and the Sunspot Spectrum* (submitted in August 1921), Russell examined carefully the "case of the missing elements" as I termed it in an earlier chapter. His opening remarks make clear his objective. He says:

> Dr. Megh Nad Saha, in an important series of papers, has shown the great importance of the modern thermodynamic theory of ionisation in astro-physical and spectroscopic researches. In particular, he makes certain predictions about the behaviour of the lines of alkali metals in the spectra of sun-spots. The present communication deals with certain points connected with the theory, especially when many kinds of atoms are present at the same time ...

Saha took an extremely simple model for the chromosphere. For example, if one considers the element calcium, then the chromosphere is made up of only three gases: (i) a gas of neutral Ca atoms, (ii) a gas of Ca^+ ions, and (iii) a gas of electrons. Implicitly, Saha assumed that the electrons all came from the ionisation of Ca alone, whereas in reality the electron could have come from the ionisation of any one of the species to be found in the stellar atmosphere. So Russell first extended Saha's formula to the case where many atomic species are present. Next he dealt with successive ionisation, i.e., $M \rightarrow M^+ \rightarrow M^{++} \rightarrow \ldots$, (which Saha also had considered while dealing with stars).

Having lined up all the formulae required, the next job was to look at observational data. For this, Russell turned to Mount Wilson. Saha too turned to Mount Wilson but for him the doors were closed. Russell, however, could walk right in and help himself. In fact, his good friend Walter Adams had already recorded precisely the data Russell now needed. So it was a cakewalk and Russell was able to record:

> The main features of the behaviour of the lines of the alkali metal in sun-spots, as Saha has shown. may be accounted for by the relative ease of ionisation, sodium being considerably ionised, potassium still more, and rubidium completely so, except in sun-spots ... The data detailed above ... are all in striking agreement with Dr. Saha's theory ...

One does feel sorry for Saha, but however sympathetic we might feel we should not quite blame Russell. The data came from Mount Wilson and it was George Hale, the Director of the Observatory who ignored Saha and not Russell. The latter was quite generous with his compliments, and concluding his paper Russell wrote:

> The principles of ionisation theory [of Saha] will evidently be of great importance throughout the whole world of astrophysics, and Dr. Saha has made an application of the highest interest to the question of the physical meaning of the sequence of stellar spectra ...
>
> The possibilities of the new method appear to be very great. To utilize it fully, years of work will be required to study the behaviour of the elements mentioned above and of others, in the stars, in laboratory spectra, and by the direct measurement of ionisation; but the prospect of increase of our knowledge, both of atoms and of stars, as a result of such researches, makes it urgently desirable that they should be carried out.

In later years, Saha often quoted this last para. Russell did not stop with the Sun; he tackled stellar spectra also but that story comes a little later.

5.7 A lawyer for Saha

Shortly after Saha published his paper, an astronomer named Plaskett reported an exhaustive study of stars of the O-type. The stars examined formed a sequence and as one went down the line, some spectral lines appeared while others disappeared, etc. In his paper, Plaskett drew upon Saha's theory to deduce the temperature of the stars. But being of the view that Saha's theory was defective, he modified it and used his modified theory to draw conclusions.

Milne (whose name has already been mentioned) saw Plaskett's paper. He quickly realised that Plaskett had not properly understood Saha's work and that in the name of correcting Saha, had himself made mistakes! Writing in the journal *Observatory* he says:

Mr. Plaskett is to be congratulated on his ingenious negotiations of so many difficulties and his final arrival at a scale of temperature which to some extent commends itself. But his procedure appears to the writer to involve a considerable fallacy.

Milne offers a lengthy discussion of where and how Plaskett went wrong. He then adds:

According to Plaskett, "Saha has assumed the rate of recombination of free electrons and ionised atoms upon encounter is independent of the temperature." It is difficult to see what justification there is for this statement. The thermodynamic formula used by Saha is derived in any book on physical chemistry, and throughout such derivations it is expressly stated and taken into account that the velocities of reaction (both backwards and forwards) are functions of the temperature.

Interestingly, the temperatures that Plaskett calculates for the stars in question using his theory are not very different from those on Saha's theory but, as Milne says,

there is a fundamental difference between Plaskett's formula and Saha's. The salient point about Saha's formula is that it involves the pressure — it predicts increased ionisation at low pressure in accordance with experiment. And this is with justice claimed as its most striking success. Plaskett's formula does not involve pressure ...

Despite being highly critical of Plaskett, Milne ends his paper on a generous note. He observes:

This somewhat drastic criticism of the theoretical portions of Plaskett's work must not be taken to obscure the great admiration the writer feels for Plaskett's contribution in general, both for the thoroughness and value of the observational work and for its skillful application to the Bohr theory and to the problem of classification. The author marshals his work in a way which seems to give one a vivid acquaintance with O-type stars as physical objects, rather than as heretofore the ghostly backgrounds of a few occasional and unusual spectra.

Interestingly, Saha never referred (in his writings) either to Plaskett or to Milne rising to his (Saha's) defence.

5.8 Extensions to Saha's work

Saha made his breakthrough essentially by building a bridge. Being a voracious reader, he was conversant with modern developments including in astrophysics and atomic physics. On the other hand, as a teacher, he had a thorough grasp of thermodynamics. When Eggert's paper appeared, he knew precisely where Eggert had missed ·the bus, and wherefrom to pull the required formulae, numbers, etc. Saha did not *derive* the ionisation formula; he merely *adapted* a formula chemists routinely used. His genius lay in recognising that ionisation in the Sun and in stars is a thermally induced process and that the laws of reaction in chemistry can equally well be applied to this process. Further, his knowledge of atomic physics enabled him to quickly tap data on ionisation potentials. Once this was done, he was home. Today all this might appear simple and perhaps even obvious. But way back in 1920, things were very different. People knew about atoms, their energy levels and the origin of spectra. But nobody even thought of discussing in detail how a collection of atoms behave when heated and what it all has to do with spectra. Einstein's theory of the blackbody spectrum published in 1916 (see *Bose and His Statistics*) was the only theory to come anywhere close to the linkage between temperature, excitation of atomic energy levels and the emission and absorption of spectral lines; and pressure does not appear anywhere in Einstein's analysis. From there to where Saha went there was another *huge* conceptual gap and Saha leapt over it like Hanuman. That is what we must bear in mind and appreciate.

   Now you might be aware (especially if you have read *A Hot Story*) that thermodynamics is essentially a macroscopic science. It requires justification at the atomic or microscopic level, and that is provided by statistical mechanics. What about the thermodynamics of chemical dissociation? Did it have any blessings from statistical mechanics? Not until 1920, and it was only in that year Ehrenfest and Trkal (of Holland) did something about it. (Possibly, Saha's first paper on thermal ionisation had already appeared by then.) Meanwhile, just around this time, R.H. Fowler in collaboration with C.G. Darwin (grandson of the great explorer) had published two papers in which they "treated the usual problem of partition of energy in statistical mechanics by a more powerful method than has hitherto been used." In between Saha's paper appeared, and clearly it was destined to play an important role in astrophysics. So Fowler said to himself: "Why don't I, starting from where Ehrenfest and Trkal left off, try to derive Saha's formula from first principles, using the method Darwin and I have already developed?" Fowler quickly produced the "missing link" and it appeared in print in January 1923.

Was Fowler's result (obtained from first principles) any different from that of Saha? Yes. Fowler obtained the result

$$\log_{10} \frac{x^2}{1 - x^2} P = \frac{U}{4.517T} + 2.5 \log_{10} T - 6.5 + b(T). \qquad (5.1)$$

Here

$$b(T) = g_1 + g_2 \exp(-E_2/k_B T) + g_3 \exp(-E_3/k_B T) + \ldots \quad (5.2)$$

g_1, g_2, g_3, ... denoting the weights of the various quantum states of the atom, and E_2, E_3, ... the energies of the excited states (E_1 is taken as the zero of the energy scale). In short, a first-principle's derivation did give Saha's formula but with an extra term $b(T)$.

Fowler did not stop with (5.1); he went further and considered all the complications such as many atomic species being simultaneously present, each atomic species being capable of multiple ionisation, there being molecules which rotate and vibrate, etc. Essentially, Fowler's work provided all the firepower needed for a thorough attack on stellar atmospheres. And this attack Fowler launched in collaboration with Milne.

5.9 A fresh assault on stars

In his work on the Sun, Saha was concentrating on a single celestial object, and information was squeezed by comparing the lines due to a neutral atom M and its ionised counterpart M^+. When it came to stars, Saha had to change his tactics; also, the problem was different. He now focussed on a particular line of M, and examined how its intensity varied across the Harvard sequence. He found that the line first appeared, grew in intensity and then disappeared. Concurrently new lines appeared and began to grow and these, Saha correctly surmised, were due to M^+. Having observed all this, Saha fixed the temperature scale by noting when a particular line was on the point of just appearing or just disappearing. The logic behind this approach is not difficult to see. I mean a line due to M disappears because M has become completely ionised to M^+. But this happens at a particular temperature. Knowing the ionisation potential and taking an estimate for the pressure, this transition temperature can be calculated. In this way Saha was effectively able to declare: "When the Harvard catalogue says a star belongs to the type M_c, it means the temperature is 4000°K; when a star belongs to type G_o, the temperature is 7000°K, and so on."

This in short is how Saha converted the Harvard scale into an absolute temperature scale, and the method he employed is referred to as the method of *marginal disappearance*. While the idea is sound no doubt, there are practical difficulties, including in precisely determining when a line just disappears. So Fowler and Milne argued, why not try to fix the temperature scale by observing when the line intensity becomes a maximum? As they put it:

> The temperature at which, for a given pressure, a given line whose series relations are known attains its maximum is provided by statistical theory. Consequently, each observed maximum of a line in the stellar sequence gives a certain relation between temperature and pressure holding at the point in the sequence concerned. We submit that it is only in this way that Saha's theory can be fairly applied and strictly tested ...
>
> It is easy to calculate from Saha's theory as it stands the condition for the maximum intensity of lines like the H and K lines of calcium ... But Saha's theory has not hitherto accounted quantitatively for the maxima of such lines as the Balmer lines of hydrogen, the lines of He^+, or the line $\lambda = 4481\text{Å}$ of Mg^+ ...

This is precisely where all the extensions to Saha's formula made by Fowler came in handy. Fowler and Milne promptly went to work and what emerged was a more precise conversion of the Harvard scale into a temperature scale.

Fowler and Milne published two seminal papers, in the first of which attention was restricted to "'colder" stars. They assume that every star has a photosphere (like the Sun) and that absorption is severe in the region of stellar atmosphere just adjacent to the photosphere — at the "ground level" if you will; usually, this region is referred to as the reversing layer. In their analysis, they needed a value for P_e, the partial electron pressure in the reversing layer, and for convenience they assumed the value 1.31×10^{-4} atmosphere throughout the stellar sequence. Of course, this value is not quite pulled out of a hat but based on some detailed reasoning (which does not concern us).

OK. What did they find after all this trouble? The answer may be found in Fig.5.6. This figure shows how the intensity of spectral lines would vary as a function of T, given that P_e remains the same in all stars and is equal to 1.31×10^{-4} atmosphere. If now we mark off on the x-axis the stellar type where a particular line shows maximum intensity, then one has effectively converted the apparently arbitrary Harvard sequence into a temperature scale; this correspondence is also shown in Fig.5.6. We must here remember that this was not really the first such conversion. Much earlier, Russell had attempted the same exercise but he did not use spectroscopic data; rather

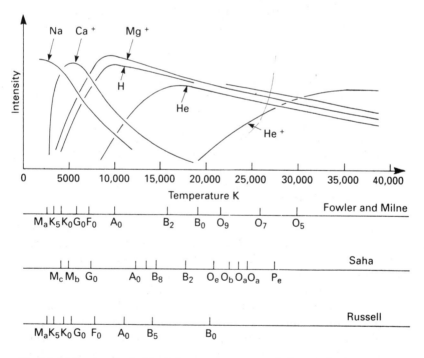

Fig.5.6 At the top is sketched the temperature variation of the intensity of various spectral lines as deduced by Fowler and Milne. Just below is shown the Harvard-temperature conversion arrived at by them. Also shown for comparison are the conversion scales of Saha and of Russell.

he depended on the colour of the star. Russell knew all along that this was not quite the way to do it and that one must somehow take account of the actual intensity of the spectral line; but he did not know the trick. Saha knew, and he performed the first legal conversion, if one might call it that. The only problem was that Saha chose to fix the scale by *judging when lines appeared or disappeared*. Fowler and Milne argued that it is far more accurate to do the conversion by *judging when the line has maximum intensity* rather than when it just fades away; and of course they had all the extensions to Saha's formula needed for the rather complex analysis. When Fowler died in 1944, Milne recalled his association with him and wrote:

> Saha had concentrated on the marginal appearances and disappearances of absorption lines in stellar sequence, assuming an order of magnitude for the pressure in a stellar atmosphere and calculating the temperature where increasing ionisation, for example, inhibited further absorption of the line in question ... As Fowler and I were one day stamping around my rooms in Trinity and discussing this, it suddenly occurred to me that the *maximum* intensity of the Balmer lines of hydrogen, for example, was readily explained by the consideration that at the lower temperatures there were too few excited atoms to give appreciable absorption, whilst at the higher temperatures there were too few neutral atoms left to give any absorption ... That evening I did a hasty order of magnitude calculation of the effect and found that to agree with a temperature of 10000° for stars of type A_0, where the Balmer lines have their maximum, a pressure of the order of 10^{-4} atmosphere was required. This was very exciting, because standard determinations of pressures in stellar atmospheres from line shifts and line widths had been supposed to indicate a pressure of the order of one atmosphere or more, and I had begun on other grounds to disbelieve this.

So now you have some idea of why Fowler and Milne preferred a particular value for P_e. Notice the low value for P_e. According to Saha, this almost suggests that the whole mass of the reversing layer of the Sun can be contained in a thimble!

What about the so-called "hotter" stars? Why did that call for a separate long paper from Fowler and Milne? The basic reason is simple. In the hotter stars, all species of atoms have greater chances of being ionised; so the concentration of electrons is higher, which means that P_e is somewhat higher, compared to that in cooler stars. This slightly higher value leads to some corrections in the temperature assignment for the hotter stars.

You might perhaps be wondering: Why all this fuss about converting an arbitary sequence of alphabets, i.e., O B A F G K M N ...

into an absolute temperature scale? What is so great about it? To appreciate the answer we must take a look at the H–R diagram (see also *Chandrasekhar and His Limit*). When the plot or map was originally made, the x-axis was just the Harvard sequence and it had no formal physical sequence. And yet there was something strange because the map showed clustering of stars. Indeed one could even draw trajectories to show the life history of a star of a particle mass, and dots on the map clinging to the line represent different stars in different stages of evolution in this particular sequence. It is here that Saha's quotation of Sir John Herschel becomes pertinent. In a nutshell, thanks to the conversion of the Harvard scale into a temperature scale, one could now read a lot of meaning into the H–R diagram, particularly with regard to stellar evolution.

5.10 Some footnotes

Saha made his discovery roughly three quarters of a century ago, and to a modern astrophysicist, much of it is all "old hat". As a preparation for this book I thumbed through many recent volumes on astrophysics and found that Saha's work is not even mentioned in some of them! Others do so but barely in passing. One can't, however, complain too much about this apparent indifference because current interests are very different from what they were in the twenties. Indeed, change of fashions is a perpetual phenomenon and there is nothing special about astrophysics — it happens in all subjects all the time. But when I went back to the astrophysical literature of the early twenties, it was an altogether different story because so *many* papers then drew inspiration from Saha's pioneering work. By the thirties, some of this work had expanded and branched off so much that people had already stopped referring to Saha! For example, I saw a paper by Russell published in 1934 entitled *Molecules in the Sun and Stars*. People had discovered that the spectral lines of the Sun and the stars indicated not only the presence of atoms (in various stages of ionisation), but even molecules like CO, TiO, SiO, N_2, ... Meanwhile, laboratory experiments had revealed a wealth of information about molecular spectra and thanks to the advent of quantum mechanics one also knew a lot about the (quantum) theory of molecular spectra. Taking advantage of all this and of course the new trend set by Saha, Russell was able to compare theoretical estimates of the abundances of various molecules in celestial bodies with values obtained from spectroscopic studies (of the stars). Quite a big leap forward. However, no citation of Saha's work; it was now taken for granted

— after all, do we always mention Newton's name even though we use his laws?

As I mentioned before, between 1920 and 1930, investigators led by Russell really squeezed the juice out of Saha's formula. Mount Wilson was the prime centre of activity — naturally — but there were also others in the act. One name which deserves special mention is that of Cecilia Payne-Gaposchkin who worked at the Harvard Observatory. Let us hear some of her recollections. Describing how she got into this business she says:

> In my last year at Cambridge [she was in Cambridge for a spell before coming to Harvard] I had come to know E.A. Milne, who (with Ralph Fowler) had just published the historic paper on stellar atmospheres. They in turn had been inspired by the brilliant idea with which Meghnad Saha had applied the principles of physical chemistry to the ionisation of stellar material, the idea that gave birth to modern astrophysics. [Note!] Before I left Cambridge, Milne told me that if he had my opportunity [in Harvard], he would go after the observations that would test and verify the Saha theory. When I told Dr. Shapely [then Director of Harvard Observatory] that this was what I should like to do, he promptly opened up to me the riches of the Harvard plate collection [in those days one did not have photographic film but photographic glass plates]. I was alarmed at the thought of handling such priceless material. What if I should break one of the plates? "Well," he said, "you can keep the pieces!" When a little later I inadvertantly sat down on a pile of plates, I rushed out of the Observatory and did not dare to return for several days. Fortunately no damage has been done.

Cecilia Payne also records a visit to her observatory by Saha. She says:

> In the early days of astrophysics it was natural that Meghnad Saha should visit us. He left a clear picture of a great and simple personality. He told me that his whole life had been changed as a result of reading *The Cloister and the Hearth*. Before that time he had believed that a celibate life was the best; but the book had resolved him to marry. How strange that a Victorian author should so influence an oriental! On another occasion he had mentioned that he had better not die in the United States. Mystified, I asked him why not? He replied, "Because I am a Parsee. My body must be placed on a tower for the vultures."

I wonder how Payne took Saha to be a Parsee! Was she confusing him with someone else or was Saha teasing her? We would never know.

And so we come to the end of a great scientific story (not Saha's life story yet, because there are big chunks of it left still). The most remarkable part of it is that so much information was squeezed simply by *looking* at stars. I always find this incredible. Today's situation is even more astounding, for not only have telescopes vastly improved since those days but we now have various kinds of telescopes like radio telescopes, infrared telescopes, X-ray telescopes and gamma-ray telescopes. As if all these were not enough, we even have orbiting telescopes! What a tremendous amount has been learnt about objects billions and billions of kilometres away!! Sometimes, I wonder whether I should wonder about stars (as the nursery rhyme recommends) or about man's ingenuity.

6   Back To India

6.1 Summons from Sir Ashutosh

As we saw before, Saha had a wonderful scientific exposure in Europe. But curiously (as happened also in the case of Bose), he did not do anything new or highly original during his stay there. Perhaps he was busy soaking in experience, which notwithstanding his low productivity during this period was no doubt very beneficial. Time was flying and the travel fellowships were drawing to a close. At this stage Saha received a letter from Sir Ashutosh Mookerjee informing him that a new Chair in Physics (Khaira Professorship) had been created which would be offered to him if he would return immediately. Saha promptly did so but to his dismay discovered that Calcutta was not what it used to be; the working conditions had considerably deteriorated. How was that possible with Sir Ashutosh in command? Because Sir Ashutosh was now having problems with the Bengal Government!

As I told you earlier, Sir Ashutosh came to the University like a fresh breeze, collecting funds, starting departments, revising curricula, etc. Everyone was happy but not the Government (don't ask me why; they are like that!). Particularly unhappy was the Governor Lord Ronaldshay, also the Chancellor of the University. Like a tiger in the bushes he was waiting for an opportunity and it came when Sir Ashutosh turned finally to the Government for running expenses. And now the tiger began to smack its lips!

Net result: The University was in deep financial trouble and there were times when Sir Ashutosh did not know how he was going to pay salaries. Saha was caught up in this turmoil and where he was concerned, he could not get an assistant, he could not buy equipment and he even had problems about lab space. (Raman who was there at the same time did not have such a rough experience because he did all his research elsewhere — see *Raman and His Effect*.) Much as he loved Calcutta, Saha could not take this punishment and around 1923 or so he decided to leave.

6.2 Goodbye Calcutta

By now Saha had achieved some reputation and when it became known that he wanted to leave, he promptly received offers from the Aligarh Muslim University and the Banaras Hindu University. But he rejected them both in favour of another from the Allahabad University, chiefly because some of his good friends were on the Executive Council of that University. Even so it was no cake walk because some others on the Council objected to his appointment, and one person even went so far as to say that he had received an adverse report on Saha. But what swung the day was the favourable opinion on Saha's work expressed by Einstein, Eddington and Russell. Thus it was that around 1923 or so Saha became the University Professor of Physics in Allahabad.

6.3 The Allahabad experience

Allahabad was no doubt quite different from Calcutta but on the whole, life was no better. Saha stepped into a literal vacuum and *everything* had to be built up from scratch, which was a tedious grind. Everywhere there were people who wielded power but had little appreciation of academics; all they did was to obstruct (alas, seventy years later, the situation is no better in most of our Universities and research centres). For example, Saha ordered many new books for the Library as it had mostly ancient publications. The University Treasurer, one Mr. Dave and a former High Court Judge saw the order and came to the Library. He asked Saha: "Have you read all these books available in the Library?" Saha said, "No, and nobody can do it." The Treasurer then triumphantly asked, "In that case, why are you asking for grants for making fresh purchases? Better read the books available and after you have finished ask for money for new books." Can you believe that! I wonder what kind of a Judge this person was. The tragedy is that such ignoramuses still abound and they wield so much authority.

To get back to Saha's story, he desperately wanted to build up a lab and do all sorts of experiments on thermal ionisation. This needed money but none was available. In fact, he had a hard time buying equipment even for the B.Sc. and M.Sc. classes. I don't know whether they still use such instruments but in my days there was one instrument called the Post Office Box used in experiments on electricity. Saha ordered a dozen of these and promptly bureaucracy was up in arms. Why were twelve Post boxes needed for one building? Would not one do? The bureaucrats mistook the instrument for the box used for receiving mail. It didn't occur to them to check with Saha or accept that he was not exactly a fool and would therefore not make a stupid mistake. Giving hell was and continues to be a favourite pastime of administrators; of course, it is always cleverly disguised as meticulous discharge of duty. In 1926, Saha was elected a Fellow of the Royal Society (FRS). This was a big boost for Saha and the University as well. However, Saha's problems remained what they were. But there was one silver lining in the form of a congratulatory letter from Sir Williams Morris, the Governor of the United Provinces (which is what Uttar Pradesh was then known as). Saha thanked the Governor, and learning that he was once the classfellow of Lord Rutherford, took the opportunity to tell him about the poor state of the lab. The Governor was moved and immediately sanctioned a research grant of Rs. 5,000/- per year. It was by no means a princely sum but something was better than nothing.

Saha wanted more money and he persuaded Sir Tej Bahadur Sapru, an eminent citizen of Allahabad to write to the Central Government in Delhi recommending a research grant. The request wound its way to a bureaucrat who sat on it for *two* years at the end of which he asked: "Why should the Central Government give a grant to a project being done in a University in a Province?" In desperation, Saha then turned to the Royal Society. Understanding his plight, the Society promptly sanctioned 1500 and at last Saha was able to make a beginning with his experiments. Incidentally, by the time all this happened, it was 1931 — so it took Saha only *eight* years to get some measly grants.

Despite the severely adverse circumstances, Saha kept up his courage and poured his heart into teaching. Slowly good students gathered and Saha began to find some satisfaction. Realising the paucity of good books by Indian authors, he wrote a classic, *A Textbook of Heat* which I studied as a student and which for many years was used in several other countries as well as a textbook. Among Saha's students, two deserve special mention namely, D.S. Kothari and R.C. Majumdar. Later they both moved to Delhi University and founded the Physics Department there which year after year turned out brilliant students of theoretical physics. I can vouch for this because I know many of these physicists personally. And it all goes back to Saha.

6.4 Physics in Allahabad

What about research? It must be said to Saha's credit that whereas lesser mortals might have just quit in sheer disgust and desperation, Saha kept his chin up and in fact managed a reasonable number of publications. Maybe they were not as epoch making as some of his earlier ones but to have published anything at all was in itself a great achievement. Saha's contributions during the Allahabad period fall under three broad categories. Firstly, he got deeply engrossed in explaining what was called complex spectra, i.e., the intricate details of the spectra of complex atoms like say iron. The twenties had witnessed the emergence of a new approach in physics, namely quantum mechanics (see *The Quantum Revolution:* Part I) and at long last reliable tools were available to explain the mysteries of the atom. But this did not mean that interpreting spectra was a trivial affair. On the contrary it was a most tedious task, as a myriad details had to be kept in view. Indeed, one is amazed that Saha became preoccupied with such an intricate problem; perhaps he felt a nasty physics problem was the best antidote to the nasty problems he was experiencing as a professor! Now the explanation of complex spectra was a challenging task that attracted many of the best brains but, unlike his European counterparts, Saha had to work alone and under hostile circumstances. No wonder that in the end he was beaten to the post by Hund (of Europe). History may remember Hund as the one who explained complex spectra but we should remember Saha as the one who showed how not to give up even against the greatest odds.

Let us now turn to the experiment that Saha finally managed to perform, after going through enormous trouble to get money and equipment. By mental make up, Saha was basically a theoretician and there is no evidence to suggest that he possessed the peculiar restlessness, improvisation ability and drive that gifted experimentalists (e.g., J.C. Bose and C.V. Raman) have. Mind you, this is no reflection on Saha's abilities; just that as in other walks of life, people are made differently — I mean, if you take cricket as an example, don't we have fast bowlers, spin bowlers, attacking batsmen, defensive batsmen and so on? The same in science and in fact it is this diversity which is responsible for the richness of science.

Saha's first brush with experiments was in the early twenties when he was in Berlin. While there, he tried to set up an apparatus in which elements like Na, Rb and Cs could be heated to high temperatures to produce vapours. Saha wanted to measure simultaneously the electrical conductivity of the vapour and the spectrum emitted by it. At relatively low temperatures, the vapour would consist only of neutral atoms and the electrical conductivity would be zero; and the spectral lines too would be characteristic of the neutral atom. As T is raised there would be increasing ionisation and a corresponding change in the character of the spectral lines. In this way, Saha hoped to obtain detailed information about the temperature-dependence of the spectral lines, the conductivity being a measure of the extent of ionisation. I am sure you would appreciate how useful such data would be in interpreting stellar spectra.

Saha could not complete this work in Germany and tried to do so on return to Calcutta. A short paper was published by him in the Journal of the Science Department of the University but it is a rather disappointing one. Barring some qualitative observations, the paper contains no worthwhile results. But we must remember that this was precisely the period when the University as a whole was being given the works by the Bengal Government; quite possibly therefore, Saha was not able to do all that he wanted.

Moving over to the Allahabad part of the story, once he had some money Saha set up an experiment to measure the electron affinity of chlorine. The atoms of many elements, especially the halogens (i.e., fluorine, chlorine, bromine and iodine) have a tendency to grab an electron and become negative ions (you can find out for yourself the reason why). When an electron is picked up by the neutral halogen atom, a certain amount of energy is also liberated, i.e.,

$$X + e \rightarrow X^- + E.$$

This energy E is called the *electron* affinity. Many problems, especially in chemistry, demanded a knowledge of the value of E and there was therefore a need for measuring it experimentally. And Saha devised a method which required an application of his formula.

The principle of his method is briefly as follows: Suppose NaCl is heated in a furnace. It will then dissociate, but there are two ways in which this can happen, they being:

(i) NaCl $\leftrightarrow$ Na$^+$ + Cl$^-$ + D

(ii) NaCl $\leftrightarrow$ Na$^+$ + Cl$^-$ $-$ Q.

Observe that both reactions can go forward as well as backward. The atoms and ions have their own reactions, they being

(iii) Na $\leftrightarrow$ Na$^+$ + e $-$ I

(iv) Cl + e ↔ Cl⁻ + E.

In short, when NaCl is heated to a sufficiently high temperature and equilibrium is established, the vapour would have a certain amount of Na, Cl, Na⁺ and Cl⁻. Now the four quantities D, Q, I and E are related to each other by

$$E = D + I - Q.$$

Of these, the values of D and I were already known. If Q could be measured then the value of E is determined — this was Saha's idea.

Figure 6.1 shows a rough schematic of the arrangement employed by Saha to determine Q. G is a graphite furnace in which is introduced the salt that is to be vapourised. When sufficiently heated, positive and negative ions issue out through the hole. Placed in front of it is a Faraday cup which is essentially a device to collect charge and measure the current. If a positive potential is applied to the cup (with respect to the furnace), the negative ions would be collected. Similarly, the positive ions are collected by applying a negative voltage, and in this way the currents $i(Na^+)$ and $i(Cl^-)$ are measured. In turn these determine the partial pressures $p(Na^+)$ and $p(Cl^-)$; knowing these and the total vapour pressure p, a formula like the one we wrote earlier can be used to arrive at the value of Q. Using KCl and NaCl Saha obtained the value 86.6 kilocalories/mole for the electron affinity of Cl which compared favourably with the value of 86.5 deduced earlier by theoretical analysis by Born and Mayer.

Perhaps the most interesting piece of work done by Saha in Allahabad relates to the atmosphere. Have you ever wondered how we in India are able to receive radio signals from say, the BBC in London? You probably know the answer and might say: "Where is the problem? The electromagnetic waves radiated from London are bounced back by the upper layers of our atmosphere, and what we pick up is the reflected signal. The curvature of the Earth poses no difficulty." Very true. In that case, why can't we receive TV signals directly from London and why do we have to depend on satellite relay? May be you know the answer to that one too. Well in any case, what happens to TV signals is that they cannot bounce back like radio signals do; the atmosphere is transparent to them. That is why one employs a geostationary satellite way above the Earth to catch the escaping TV signals and relay them back.

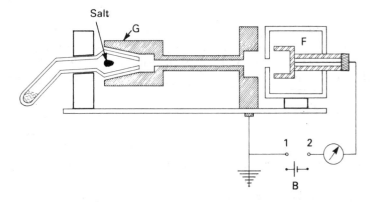

Fig.6.1 Schematic of the experimental set up used by Saha for measuring the electron affinity of chlorine. G is a graphite furnace. The salt is placed in a bent iron tube which is inserted into the furnace. The tube is bent so that molten salt can run down and not interfere. The beam of ions and atoms issuing out travel to the right. Here the ions are collected by the Faraday cup F and the current is measured. The type of ion collected is determined by how the battery B is connected to the two terminals 1 and 2.

The upper atmosphere thus has its own peculiar way of dealing with electromagnetic waves incident on it. Depending on the frequency of the incident wave, it either reflects it or transmits it. Several questions now arise:

1. Where exactly in the atmosphere do those reflections take place?
2. How are the reflecting layers formed?
3. How exactly do they affect electromagnetic waves?
4. What is the filtering action, if any, on the light coming to us from the Sun?

Upper atmosphere is the generic name given to the part of the atmosphere above the stratosphere (i.e., above say 20 km). Actually, there is precious little air out there, but nevertheless very interesting and crucial physical processes happen in this tenuous region. Various methods have been employed to explore it and they include:

1. Sending instruments up in balloons.
2. Study of the spectrum of the night sky.
3. Study of the reflection of radio waves.
4. **Study of the ozone content and its geographical as well as seasonal variations.**

5. Observation of the daily, seasonal and yearly variation of the Earth's magnetic field.

As early as 1886, Schuster made the suggestion that ultraviolet radiation from the Sun was in some way affecting the upper atmosphere (in those days, they did not know about ionisation). Then came the radio and the discovery of various reflecting layers (of which the most prominent are the socalled E and F layers). Saha's interest in this matter appears to have been aroused by results on radio wave reflection obtained by his students, particularly Toshniwal.

Saha addressed himself to two questions: Firstly, what really goes on in the upper atmosphere? From the reflection of radio waves one knew there were layers of ions, but how were they produced? Incidentally, because of the presence of ions, the upper atmosphere is also referred to as the *ionosphere*. The second question that attracted him was: How do electromagnetic waves propagate in the upper atmosphere? The latter problem is mainly mathematical in nature but far more interesting from a physics point of view is the first question. Indeed in tackling it, Saha did some intelligent speculative work worth recalling.

What is the nature of the upper atmosphere? Let us turn to Saha for an answer:

> The chief constituents of the upper atmosphere are molecular O_2 and N_2 and probably atomic O and N; hydrogen appears to be definitely excluded, and no helium has yet been found. Even if it exists, the argument will not be much changed. Ozone [O_3] has been found to be confined between 20 km to 50 km and undoubtedly plays some important part in the phenomena observed in the lower layers.

Next let us consider the radiation emitted by the Sun. We usually describe it as a blackbody corresponding to a temperature of 6000°K (see *Bose and His Statistics* for a description of blackbody radiation). However, since the early part of this century it was known that radiation coming from the Sun and having a wavelength $\lambda < 2900$ A did not reach the Earth, i.e., there was a cut off — see Fig. 6.2. It was natural to assume that these ultraviolet photons are in some manner absorbed and eventually cause the ionisation of N_2 and O_2 molecules. Thus the ionised layers of the upper atmosphere were believed to be formed due to photochemical reactions induced by the photons in the "*UV* tail" of the blackbody spectrum of the Sun. A nice idea but there is a problem, as Saha pointed out; there were *too few* photons in the tail to produce the requisite amount of ionisation. As he put it: "If the Sun be supposed to radiate like a blackbody at a temperature of 6000°K, it is incapable of ionising N_2 ...". In that case, how was the ionisation produced and where did the required *UV* photons come from? That is where Saha's cleverness shows.

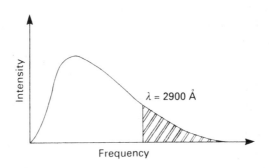

Fig.6.2 Blackbody spectrum of the Sun and the observed ultraviolet cutoff.

To answer the question just posed, Saha went back to the Sun. Earlier I told you that the photosphere radiates a blackbody spectrum and that some wavelengths are selectively absorbed in the chromosphere to produce a Fraunhofer spectrum. If all the photons at some particular wavelength, say λ_i, are absorbed, the corresponding Fraunhofer line would be perfectly black; but in the observed spectrum, the lines are not black. This would mean that there is some radiation present at wavelength λ_i. Looking at Fig.6.3 you might now argue: "OK, some photons at λ_i are absorbed and say they are reemitted. You still can't get more photons of λ_i than you started with in the blackbody spectrum." Actually there could be more photons but the arguments are slightly involved and so let me go over them slowly.

Consider a hydrogen atom in the solar chromosphere. We have already discussed the line spectrum of H in an earlier chapter but for our present purposes, a portion is shown in Fig. 6.4(a). Radiation of frequency $\nu_{13}(=\nu_{31})$ forming a part of the blackbody spectrum issuing from the photosphere will be absorbed by the hydrogen atom, resulting in the transition 1→3. The H-atom is now in an excited state and it deexcites via the cascade 3→2 followed by 2→1 rather than by the direct jump 3→1. In other words, while the blackbody spectrum is depleted at frequency ν_{13}, it is enriched at ν_{23} and ν_{12} which are respectively the Balmer H_α and Lyman L_α line frequencies — see Fig.6.4(b). This is not the only process;

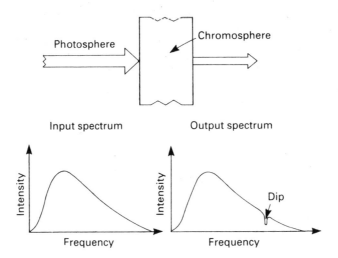

Fig.6.3 This shows how the continuous spectrum while traversing the chromosphere experiences depletion at the atomic absorption frequencies. One expects this to manifest as dips.

there are many others and in a nutshell, the ultraviolet part of the blackbody spectrum is swept and packaged into half a dozen lines, including L_α and H_α. As Saha puts it:

> By this process, ultraviolet light coming from the photosphere is *dammed* by H-atoms and converted into line radiation, and the net effect is that the resultant spectrum will show extraordinary strength for L_α and H_α.

See Fig.6.4(c). How much is the enhancement? Saha estimates that at L_α wavelength ($\lambda = 1215$Å), the line emission intensity is $\sim 40,000$ times that of the blackbody spectrum at that same wavelength. If one goes to a shorter wavelength (say around 600Å), the enhancement is about a million. Saha then shows that "some of these rays [i.e., L_α and its companions] can not only maintain the necessary ionisation but can also account for special features of the night spectrum." These details being rather complex, I shall skip them. It suffices to say that the ionisation of N_2 into N_2^+ is satisfactorily explained.

What about ozone (O_3)? How is it produced? Ozone arises in the following manner: First the oxygen molecule absorbs a photon and is raised to an excited state, i.e.,

$$O_2 + h\nu \rightarrow O_2^*$$

where O_2^* denotes an oxygen molecule in an excited state. The O_2^* collides with a normal molecule of O_2 and this leads to the collision reaction

$$O_2^* + O_2 \rightarrow O_3 + O + \text{energy.}$$

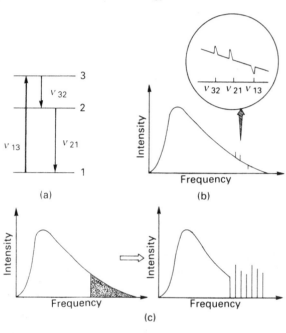

Fig.6.4 This figure illustrates Saha's hypothesis about how the *UV* part of the solar spectrum gets "repackaged". (a) shows some of the transitions in hydrogen. Photon of frequency ν_{13} is absorbed and in its place appear photons of frequencies ν_{32} and ν_{21}. The resultant modification to the spectrum is illustrated in (b). Many such processes are possible in the *UV* and the net result is, according to Saha, that the *UV* tail is swept away, all the intensity being concentrated in a few select lines. This is schematically shown in (c).

So the formation of ozone also finds a satisfactory explanation. Of course, all this is crucially dependent on the "damming" hypothesis about which Saha says:

This conclusion [damming idea], *to which it is difficult to see any alternative*, brings out the necessity of investigating the ultra-violet emission of the sun with greater care than has hitherto been done ... It appears probable that if we could observe the solar spectrum outside the atmosphere of the earth, it would appear very much like those of planetary nebulae, i.e., composed of a faint continuous background superimposed with bright emission lines of H, He and He^+ ...

About a year later in a note entitled *A Stratosphere Solar Observatory* published in the Harvard College Observatory Bulletin, Saha explicitly suggested the observation of the solar spectrum at a height greater than 40 km, possibly by lifting a spectrograph in a balloon. This way one could get out of the atmosphere and avoid the *UV* depletion it causes. Way back in 1937, Saha's idea seemed like an idle dream. But during the Second World War, the Germans developed the V2 rocket which could go up to 150 km. After the war, American scientists used captured German V2 rockets for many of their high-altitude experiments. In one such experiment conducted in 1952, the Sun's *UV* spectrum was photographed at a height of 80 km. The continuous background was absent (in the *UV* region) but prominently visible was the L_α, exactly as Saha had forecast fifteen years earlier — see Fig. 6.4(c). In more recent times, several satellite observatories have been established, the most spectacular venture being the recently launched Hubble telescope. In a nutshell, despite the unfavourable climate in Allahabad, Saha eminently succeeded in retaining his scientific spirit and even managed some useful contributions.

6.5 Saha and Academies

From around the early thirties onwards, Saha considerably widened his interests and among other things, became concerned about the Indian scientific community as a whole. He realised that the community created the scientific ambience to a certain extent and unless it was strong and vigorous, research could not flourish in the country. And the best way of nourishing and protecting the interests of the scientific community was through a suitable science academy.

The first Academy was established in Athens in a beautiful garden which belonged to one Academus. The philosopher Plato held here regularly gatherings of intellectuals for nearly fifty years and this came to be known as the Academy. The Academy founded by Plato survived for nearly three hundred years.

The type of Academy Saha was interested in was a *science* academy. Such bodies came into existence in Europe after the Renaissance, the famous ones being the Royal Society in England, the French Academy in Paris, the Prussian Academy in (what is today known as) Germany and the Russian Academy in St. Petersburg (later Leningrad and still later St. Petersburg again!). Saha felt that the United Provinces needed an Academy. The idea came to him in 1930 when the Indian Science Congress met in Allahabad. Delivering an address on the occasion, the Governor Sir Malcolm Hailey said that if a scientific body could motivate research in the University departments and steer it for public benefit, then it might become possible for the Government to offer grants for research. Saha took the hint and thanks to his efforts the U.P. Academy of Sciences came into existence in 1932; it was duly inaugurated by the Governor who had himself earlier suggested its creation. Despite the economic depression then prevailing, the Governor sanctioned an annual grant of Rs.4000/- to the Academy. Saha delivered a thought-provoking address on the occasion, in which he pointed out how while scientific advances made the world closely knit, the politicians remained primitive in their thinking. And out of this inability to keep pace came mistrust, fear and eventually wars. Saha said:

> Those who are called upon to guide the destinies of nations are mostly men with a rigid outlook, quite unfit to fathom the depths of present-day troubles or analyse the intricacies of political and economic issues, and are unable to hold out any programme of reconstruction. In our country, the result is *competitive communalism*; among free nations — a tense atmosphere of competitive nationalism, and between the ruler and subject nations — a spirit of revolt against aggressive imperialism.

All this, decades before jet planes, satellite communication and computer networks truly shrank the world. Alas, sixty years later, after one disastrous World War and a couple of vicious miniwars, the politicians are no wiser.

In 1934, the U.P. Academy of Sciences was renamed the National Academy of Sciences, a name it has retained to this day. In 1938, Saha organised a symposium on "Power Supply" under the auspicies of the Academy and requested Nehru to inaugurate it. I should mention here that thanks to some political reforms introduced by the British in 1935, elections were held in the various Provinces and the Congress was swept to power. In U.P., Nehru headed the popular government. Nehru told his audience that "the expert scientist is not always a helpful person". What he meant was that the scientist often did not realise that "things which have to be put before the Government must be definite and be related to what is actually happening. The proposals must fit in with the realities of the situation."

Nehru's remark provoked a positive response and the Academy put forward concrete suggestions concerning the generation and distribution of electric power in U.P. Proposing a vote of thanks, Saha said:

> It was in the fitness of things that Pandit Jawaharlal Nehru has agreed to preside over this annual gathering of scientists in India. His position in the country can be described by a phrase which Americans use with respect to Abraham Lincoln: First in War and first in Peace [actually, it is George Washington who is thus referred to and not Lincoln]. Next to Mahatma Gandhi, he occupies the first place in the hearts of three hundred and fifty million countrymen. [That was the population of *undivided* India then. Out of that India has since been carved India, Pakistan and Bangladesh. And our population now exceeds eight hundred million!] The time has now come for him [Nehru] to give a lead in peace-time work of reconstruction and consolidation of the country.

As it turned out, World War II intervened and nine years had to pass before India emerged free and Nehru became Prime Minister.

Despite its name National Academy of Sciences, the Allahabad Academy essentially functioned as a regional body. Saha now wanted an organisation with an all-India character and thus in 1934 he proposed the founding of an Indian Academy of Sciences. On this issue there was a strong difference of opinion between him and Raman and eventually Raman announced in Bangalore the founding of the Indian Academy of Sciences. This was unacceptable to Saha who continued his efforts and as a result there came into existence in 1935 the National Institute of Sciences, India with its headquarters in Calcutta. On Saha's initiative the headquarters was shifted to New Delhi in 1944–45. Later the name was changed to the Indian National Science Academy, the name by which it is known today.

6.6 Relief from the oppression

There were two spells when Saha could escape from the oppressive atmosphere of Allahabad. The first came in 1927 when the Italian Government organised a grand International Conference to commemorate the birth centenary of Alexandre Volta (find out who he was!). The venue was the beautiful city of Como on the shores of Lake Como at the foot of the Italian Alps, and the principal organiser was Fermi. Since the conference came close on the heels of monumental discoveries (see *The Quantum Revolution:* Part I), all the superstars were duly invited; Saha received an invitation on the strength of his earlier contributions.

At Como Saha presented a paper on the analysis of complex spectra, that being then the topic of his interest. From Como Saha proceeded to Oslo in Norway to join an expedition organised by Prof. L. Vegard of Oslo University to observe a forthcoming total solar eclipse. For this purpose, the party journeyed to Ringebu (68°N), North of the Arctic circle.

The second opportunity to go abroad came in 1936 when Saha received a fellowship from the Carnegie Trust of the British Empire. This outing was quite extended and took Saha to many places.

He left Bombay for Basra in Iraq by ship. From Basra he travelled to Baghdad by train. Iraq was the first stop because Saha very much wanted to visit the ruins of the Chaldean Empire. If physics was his first love, history was the second, particularly ancient history. Once during a meeting of the Executive Council (of which Saha was now a member), there was a prolonged discussion on the syllabus for Ancient Indian History. Saha intervened and made some remarks but the Vice Chancellor was annoyed and asked what would a scientist know about history. Instead of retorting, Saha respected the chair and immediately became silent. Later someone informed the Vice Chancellor that Saha was actually very well informed in history, whereupon the Vice Chancellor graciously apologised to Saha.

Getting back to Saha's overseas trip, after visiting various historical sites in the middle east (in Iraq, Syria, Jordan and the then Palestine), he sailed from Haifa (then in Palestine and now in Israel) for Trieste in Italy. The next stop was Munich, where there was a happy reunion with Sommerfeld. He then proceeded to London to attend the Centenary celebrations of the Physics Society where Max Planck was the chief guest. From London he went to Oxford and spent a month in the company of Milne. Crossing the Atlantic he then made his way to the Harvard College Observatory in Boston. Here he came into contact with many scientists who were actively engaged in putting his formula to practical use and who until then were just names. Among those he met were Harlow Shapley, Director of the Harvard College Observatory, Russell, Donald Menzel and Cecilia Payne-Gaposchkin. Moving west, he made a grand tour visiting many observatories and meeting famous people like Hubble (famous for his studies on the expanding universe), Adams (see Chapter 5), now Director of the Mount Wilson Observatory, and Slipher (well known for his work on the atmosphere of planets). The last western stop was the laboratory of E.O. Lawrence in Berkeley. Saha and Lawrence had met earlier in Copenhagen in the twenties but by now Lawrence was famous as the inventor of the cyclotron (for which he received the Nobel Prize). This contact proved useful and later Lawrence helped Saha to some extent to build a cyclotron in Calcutta. From Berkeley Saha turned back East, stopping in Chicago to visit the Yerkes Observatory in the vicinity (— for many years, Chandrasekhar was at Yerkes). Returning to Harvard, he attended the centenary celebrations of the Harvard University. It was then he wrote the short note proposing a stratosphere observatory (see section 6.4). While in Boston, he also visited the famous Massachussetts Institute of Technology (M.I.T.) of which K.T. Compton (brother of A.H. Compton of Compton effect fame) was the President. Returning to Europe, he attended an international conference on nuclear physics in Niels Bohr's institute in Copenhagen. He stayed in Copenhagen for two weeks and saw how nuclear physics had now moved to centre stage, having edged out atomic physics. As we shall see in the final chapter, this influenced a change in Saha's attitude also.

It was a rather long tour but Saha returned with his intellectual batteries fully charged. Allahabad must have been a great anticlimax, and despite its familiarity, reentry into the oppressive atmosphere of Allahabad was quite a painful affair. Saha was now determined to seek a change of place. Why not go back to Calcutta, his favourite city? But then, what about a job?

6.7 To Calcutta again

As it turned out, an opening to Saha became available just around this time. You might remember from an earlier chapter that Sir Ashutosh Mookerjee had created, among other things, a Chair for Physics named Palit Professorship. Raman held that Chair from its inception in 1917 to 1934 when he left for Bangalore. The Palit Professorship was then offered to D.M. Bose. In November 1937, Sir Jagadish Chandra Bose passed away and someone was needed to manage the institute he had founded. D.M. Bose, the nephew of Sir J.C. Bose was invited to become the Director of the Bose Institute and so he resigned his post in the University. The vacant Palit Chair was now offered to Saha which he readily accepted. Thus it was that Saha returned to Calcutta in 1938 to begin what might be called the final innings. This lasted eighteen years, and that story is reserved for the final chapter.

7   *Saha And Calendar Reform*

One of the characteristic traits of Saha was his passionate advocacy of causes he strongly believed in; and this included the reform of the Indian Calendar and the World Calendar Plan.

Everyone knows what the calendar is since we use it all the time. It is, however, a bit erratic, which is why there is the helpful rhyme

> *Thirty days hath September,*
> *April, June and November, ...*

to remind us which month has how many days, etc.

The calendar we use is called the Gregorian calendar after Pope Gregory who introduced it in 1582. It has many irritating features like a particular event due to occur on a particular date may occur on any day of the week. Take, for example, our Independence Day which falls on August 15. It is supposed to be a day of reminder of the freedom struggle, the sacrifices made, etc. But many look forward to it as just another holiday and they become terribly disappointed when August 15 happens to be a Sunday. That is when they wake up to the deficiencies of the Calendar and start cursing it!

What precisely is a calendar? Saha defines it as follows:

> The calendar is a table of the days of the year divided into months and weeks, and showing the dates of the religious festivals and observances with scientific precision, and adopted to the purpose of civic life. It is an indispensible requisite of civilized life.

The idea of the calendar goes back to ancient times. It all started when man became conscious of the flux or the flow of time. (For remarks on the arrow of time, see *A Hot Story.*) Ancient man not only realised that time flows but also discovered that many phenomena recur and could thus be used as time markers. Saha describes the time markers used by ancient astronomers. They are:

1. The Revolving Heaven; which produces the succession of *day* and *night*.
2. The Moon; which on account of its motion in the heavens, produces the phenomenon of phases, and gives us the *month*.
3. The Sun; which by its apparent motion in the heavens produces seasons and gives us the *year*.

As everyone knows, (1) is due to the rotation of the Earth round its axis, and (3) is due to the revolution of the Earth in its orbit around the Sun.

Notice that there are three time markers and they are derived from three different sources, namely the Earth, Moon and the Sun. It turns out that the markers don't quite "match" with each other, and all the problems of the calendar arise precisely from this.

Going back to ancient times, wise men in all civilizations recognized that these so-called time markers could be used for ordering and organising social and religious activities and that is how almanacs and calendars were born. As Saha says:

> When human communities started organized social life in the valleys of the Indus and the Ganges (India), the Nile (Egypt), the Tigris and the Euphrates (Mesopotamia) and the Hoang Ho (China), several millenia before Christ, these phenomena [day, month and year] acquired new importance. For these early societies were founded on agriculture; and agricultural practices depend on seasonal weather conditions. With these practices, therefore, grew national and religious festivals, necessary for the growth of social life, and of civilization. People wanted to know *in advance* when to expect the new moon or the fullmoon, when most of the ancient festivals were celebrated; when to expect the onset of the winter or the monsoon; when to prepare the ground for sowing; the proper time for sowing and for harvesting. Calendars are nothing but predictions of these events and were in those days framed on the basis of past expectations.

Qualitative time markers are OK but for quantitative purposes, precise definitions of time intervals are necessary. Realising this, the ancients patiently made observations of the peculiarities of the motions of the Sun, the Moon and the Earth for thousands of years, and out of this have evolved our present notions of the day, the month and the year.

Let us start with the day. By day we mean here the period that encompasses the daylight as well as the darkness period. In ancient times, people defined the day as the time-period between sunrise to sunrise or sunset to sunset. This definition clearly has problems because this duration can depend both on the latitude as well as the time of the year. For example, there are times in the year when the Sun never rises or sets at the North Pole; it just keeps hovering around in the sky! How do you define the day in such a case?

Experience has provided a way out of this jam, and today astronomers use two measures: (i) Sidereal day and (ii) the solar day. Non-technical definitions of these are as follows: The sidereal day is the time taken by the Earth to rotate once about its axis. Suppose you ask yourself how this duration could be measured. You would probably say: "This is easy. I carefully note the position of a particular star in the (night) sky today and start a clock. I wait till tomorrow and see when that star appears at precisely the same position in the sky. For this to happen, the Earth must have gone round itself once. Once the star appears at the correct position, I stop the clock and whatever duration I get is the duration of the sidereal day." Not quite, because during this period the Earth would have moved in its orbit around the Sun! Actually there is nothing wrong with your strategy and in fact it leads to the duration of the solar day. The length of the sidereal day has to be determined somewhat differently but we shall not go into that. If you think about it a bit you will realise that the solar day is slightly longer than the sidereal day.

The duration of the solar day is not a constant and it keeps varying somewhat as the Earth goes around the Sun. So one defines a *mean* solar day. If the sidereal day is taken to be a constant (a reasonable thing to do) and its duration is taken as 24 hours, then

1 mean solar day = 24h 3m 56.555s.

For practical purposes, however, it is the mean solar day which is divided into hours, minutes and seconds as

1 mean solar day = 24 × 60 × 60 = 86,400 seconds;

this you should remember. So the sidereal day is less than 24 hours.

Next we consider the month which is essentially a lunar phenomenon. Here the basic interval is the *Lunation* or the time-period taken by the Moon to pass from one conjunction with the Sun (new moon) to the next conjunction. Measured in terms of mean solar days, the lunation period keeps varying and at the present time,

1 lunation = 29.5305881 mean solar days.

A thousand years hence, the lunation period would be slightly different.

Group photograph taken in 1916 along with Acharya Prafulla Chandra Ray (seen in the central chair). Saha is standing in the last row at the extreme left.

Picture taken during the farewell party given to Saha on the eve of his departure to UK in 1920. Saha is, naturally, seated in the middle. To his right is C.V. Raman, with his famous turban. Seated extreme left is S.N. Bose.

This picture taken in London in 1921 shows Indian research scholars along with some of the professors under whom they were working. Seated second from the left is Prof. A. Fowler, while the fourth is P.C. Ray. Saha is in the second row (standing), third from the left. In the same row fourth from the right is S.S.Bhatnagar.

Portrait of Saha taken in 1921 when he was in Berlin.

Group photo taken in 1927 in Allahabad University during the felicitations to Saha on his being elected a FRS. Saha can be seen seated, fifth from the left. To his left is the (then) Vice Chancellor, Ganganath Jha.

This picture was taken during Sommerfeld's visit to Allahabad in 1929. He is, of course, occupying the central chair and to his right is Saha.

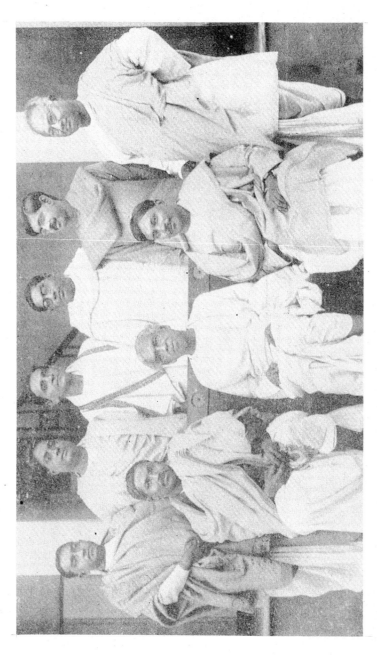

In this picture (taken in 1930), Saha (on chair, first from the left) is seen along with J.C. Bose (seated in the middle). Standing directly behind Saha (second from the left) is S.N.Bose.

Picture taken in 1936 while Saha was visiting the Harvard College. Saha, of course, cannot be mistaken; to his right is Dr. Shapley.

This picture goes back to 1936 and shows a gathering of top physicists in Neils Bohr's Institute in Copenhagen. (1) Pauli (2) Jordan (3) Heisenberg (4) Born (9) Saha (11) Bohr and (12) Bhabha.

Photo taken in Allahabad in 1938 during the visit of Sir A.S. Eddington. Saha and Eddington are, of course, easily identified. On chair at extreme left is Prof. V. Narlikar, a distinguished mathematician and relativist, and father of the well-known astrophysicist Prof. J.V. Narlikar. To the right of Saha is Sir Shah Md. Sulaiman. A judge, he was very much interested in physics and spent time with Saha whenever he could.

With Prof.C.G. Darwin, grandson of the great Charles Darwin (of *Origin of Species* fame). Photo taken in 1938 on the occasion of the Silver Jubilee of the Indian Science Congress.

What about the year? This is determined by the time required for seasonal characteristics to recur. For example, ancient Egyptians tried to define the year by observing floods in the river Nile. Today, however, we use a quantity called the *tropical year*. Unfortunately, this also keeps varying, though (mercifully!) only rather slowly. At present,

1 tropical year = 365.2421955 mean solar days.

The one major fact that emerges from all that has been said so far is that the duration of the day, the month and the year all fluctuate. That is the beginning of the problem but not all of it. What precisely are the problems of defining a calendar?

Now a calendar must, among other things, mark the year by dividing it into months and days. Further, both the year and the month must have an *integral* number of days but, as we just saw, neither the year nor the month has an integral number of days. A calendar is an attempt to solve this problem in a particular way, with minimum inconvenience. Any number of solutions have been attempted and indeed it is fascinating to study their history. As Saha says:

> A correct and satisfactory solution of these problems has not yet been obtained, though in the form of hundreds of calendars which have been used by different people of the world during historical times, we have so many *attempted* solutions.

Before we start digging into history, there is one more concept we must become familiar with and that is the *era*. We say this year is 1994, 1995 or 1996 — whatever it is. What is the meaning of, say 1994? You would say: AD 1994. AD? You would then say: Anno Domini, meaning this is the one thousand nine hundred and ninety fourth year after Christ. That's it! 1994 fixes the year concerned with respect to the Christian era; and era is needed for fixing dates in history. About eras Saha says:

> In ancient times, there was no continuous era-recording. Events were dated invariably by the years elapsed since the accession to the throne of the reigning monarch ... The continuous era-recording was first introduced by the Chaldean [Babylonian] astronomers on astrological grounds ... The first dynastic era was introduced in 312 BC by Seleucus, the general of Alexander, to commemorate his [Alexander's] conquest of Babylon ... The example of Seleucus, was followed by the Indo-Scythian kings of Afghanistan and North-West India and by Indian Kings, and this has given rise to a plethora of dynastic eras (Saka, Chedi, Gupta, Ganga, etc.) in India. This has added to the general confusion prevailing in Indian calendars.

The Christian era is supposed to have started with the birth of Christ, but it was first in use from about 500 AD, when the birth year of Christ was obtained after some research. The calculation has been shown to be wrong by a few years. A rational era-beginning should have some astronomical significance ...

Apparently Laplace did once make a concrete proposal in this respect but it did not find favour.

Now for the promised bit of history, and we start with the Egyptians for they were the first to experiment with a solar calendar, i.e., a calendar based on the Sun's movement. Incidentally, you might also glance at Fig.7.1 which indicates the appearance of various calendars. A few thousand years before Christ, the Egyptians decided

Chronological Table

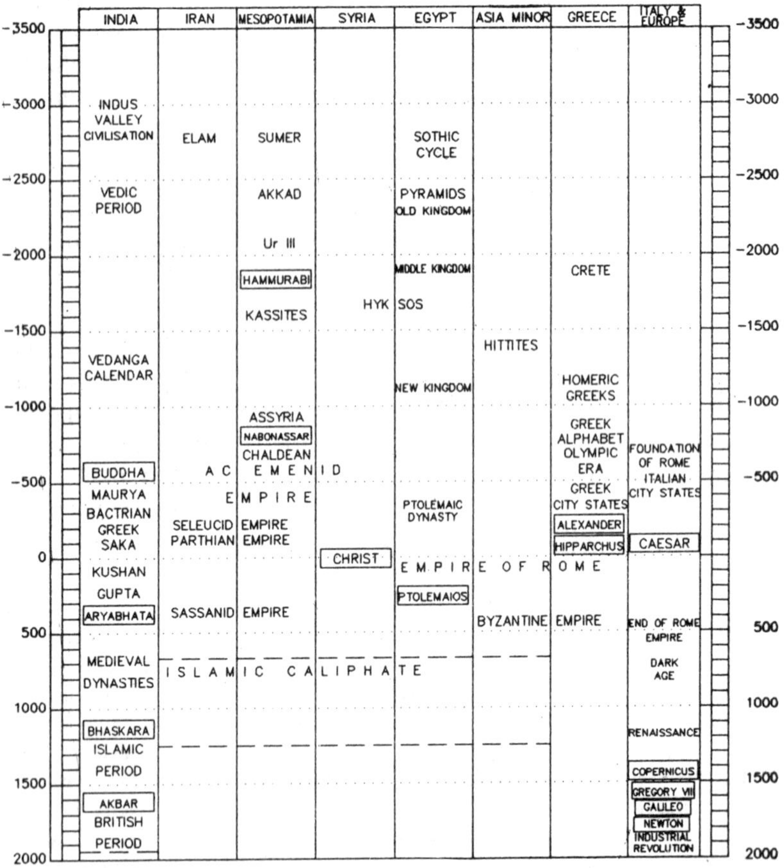

Fig.7.1 This figure reproduced from Saha's report (written with Lahiri) gives an overview of the emergence of various calendars.

that their year would have 360 days, consisting of 12 months each of exactly 30 days. Quite simple and neat but, as you would expect, the ancient Egyptians promptly ran into trouble. For example, the Nile floods did not quite recur the way expected. However, by smart observation the Egyptians found out what the trouble was and carried out what might be called the first ever calendar reform in history. They simply said: "At the end of the year, i.e., after 360 days, there shall be five days of prayer and festivities dedicated to the Gods. The new year will commence after these five days are over." The priests invented a clever myth to justify all this, but in essence what they had done was to extend the year from 360 days to 365 days.

Soon there was trouble once again and the Egyptians discovered, by some clever observations, that the correct length of the year was approximately 365 1/4 days and not 365 days as they had earlier assumed. The priests then used this duration of the year for predicting the arrival of the Nile flood but kept the knowledge to themselves. Saha comments:

> Though rather imperfect, the Egyptian Calendar was greatly admired in antiquity for its simplicity, for the length of the year and the months were fixed by definite rules, and not by officials or *pandits*. The religious observences fell on fixed days of the month and at stated hours.

On account of its simplicity, the Egyptian calendar was adopted by many nations including the Chaldeans and the Greeks. The Egyptian calendar is still in use by Christian descendants of ancient Egyptians and by the Armenian church.

Next we consider the Iranian calendar. In 520 BC the great Persian Emperor Darius (whose empire spanned several countries besides Persia) adopted and introduced the Egyptian calendar (based on the 365-day year)in his vast empire. But the astronomers of Darius improved upon the Egyptians in one important respect. They recognized that the duration of the year was actually 365 1/4 days. By approximating it as 365 days, the Egyptians made an error of (1/4) day per year (which of course they also realised later and corrected for). In 120 years, this error magnifies to one full month of 30 days. So Darius ordered that every 120 years, the calendar would have one extra month! This is rather like our tucking away one extra day in February once every four years. In fact, it is nothing but the Darius formula but spread out, one might say. In AD 648, after the Islamic conquest of Persia, the lunar calendar of Islam (Hejira) displaced the Egyptian calendar. However the Parsis who escaped to India (see the companion volume *Bhabha and His Magnificent Obsessions*) held on to the Egyptian version. In 1920,

Emperor Riza Shah Pahlavi abandoned the strictly lunar Islamic calendar and reintroduced the solar year.

We now move over to Europe and focus on what happened in France after the French Revolution. The Revolutionary Government appointed a Calendar Reform Committee to recommend a calendar based on reason rather than on religion. The Committee included, among others, the great mathematicians Laplace and Lagrange and the poet d'Eglantine. Based on his calculations on celestial mechanics, Laplace proposed that the year AD 1250 be regarded as the beginning of the French Revolutionary Era, but the calendar committee disagreed and proposed instead AD 1792, a date closer to the revolution. Clearly, sentiment proved stronger than cold scientific reasoning! The seven-day week was abandoned for a ten-day week. The month names were invented by the poet member of the calendar committee. The last five days were dedicated to the service of the poor and did not form part of any month. When Napolean became the Emperor of France, he made a deal with the Roman Catholic Church, according to which the Pope sanctioned and blessed Napolean's coronation. In return, Napolean abolished the Revolutionary Calendar (after 13 years of service) and reintroduced the Christian calendar.

This brings us to the Christian calendar. Apparently, in the beginning this calendar had nothing to do with Christianity. According to one view, this was adapted from a calendar used by tribes who lived in northern Europe long long ago. These tribes started their year in Spring (1 March) and their year had only ten months, adding in all to just 304 days. So the year ended at the time of the Winter Solstice (WS), which then occurred on December 25. (For an explanation of Solstice and other related terms, see the Appendix to this chapter.) The following 61 days were considered a period of liberation due to the onset of winter and were not counted at all! This brought them back to 1 March and a new year.

The city state of Rome also had this same calendar originally, but successive Governments kept on making minor modifications till the great Julius Caesar put the finishing touches in 46 BC , and gave us what we now know as the Julian calendar. Actually, it took a while for things to settle. Meanwhile, Caesar conquered Egypt and in the process came into contact with Egyptian astronomers. Learning from them that the year had 365 1/4 days, he introduced the idea of the leap year. Caesar found that the calendar had been mishandled for ages and thanks to ignoring the extra (1/4) day, as many as 67 days had been missed! To make good this loss and to straighten out the mess he simply inserted these 67 days between November and December in one particular year and that year came to be called the *year of confusion*! Incidentally, you can see how September, October, November and December got their names — they were respectively the seventh, eighth, ninth and the tenth month in the year, reckoning the year beginning to be March. In those days the fifth month used to be called Quintillus and in honour of Julius Caesar the name was later changed to July.

The calendar reforms introduced by Julius Caesar were not completely effected during his lifetime and some problems continued until they were straightened out by his grandson Augustus Caesar in whose honour we have now the month August. Both July and August were given the hboxstatus of major months by assigning 31 days to them.

Caesar wanted to start the new year with the Winter Solstice, i.e., on December 25 but the people resisted this choice and wanted instead the new year (i.e., 45 BC) to be started on the day of the new moon. This occurred 6 days later, i.e., on what we now call January 1. You must be wondering why I keep referring to December 25 as the Winter Solstice and not Christmas. First of course there is the elementary fact that when we are talking of Julius Caesar we are referring to a period *before* Christ. It was only in AD 500 that it was established that Christ was born on December 25!

What I have described so far is the Julian or the Roman calendar. When Christianity came to Rome, the Roman calendar survived; only, the Christians introduced their own holidays. Many of these were Jewish in origin and being mostly linked to the lunar calendar, there was an inevitable drift, one example being Easter. The calendar we use today is called the Gregorian calendar. Its history is as follows.

Now the Julian year had 365.25 days whereas the true year had a duration of 365.2422, which was slightly shorter. So the Winter Solstice which fell on December 21 in AD 323 slipped back by 10 days in 1582 and the Christmas Day appeared to be losing all its connection with the Winter Solstice. Various other discrepancies were also noted. Concerned by all this, the Roman Catholic Church deliberated on the matter and finally in AD 1582, Pope Gregory XIII published an edict revising the calendar. He ordained that Friday, October 5 of that year be counted as Friday, October 15. He further declared that centurial years not divisible by 400 were not leap years. (Thus, 1896 and 1904 were leap years but 1900 was not.) As a result, the number of leap years in 400 years was reduced from 100 to 97. The length of the calendar now stood at 365.2425 days, the error being only one day in 3333 years.

The Julian calendar as reformed by Pope Gregory came to be referred to as the Gregorian calendar and was promptly adopted by all the Catholic states of Europe, but other Christian states took longer to accept. In Great Britain it was officially introduced only in 1752. As the error had by that time amounted to 11 days, September of 1752 was shortened and 3rd September was designated as 14th September. In some countries, the Gregorian calendar was adopted only in this century. China and Albania adopted it in 1912, Bulgaria in 1916, Soviet Russia in 1918, Romania and Greece in 1924, and Turkey in 1927. This is the calendar everyone uses today for official purposes.

Perhaps this is a good juncture to say something about the seven-day week. The day, the month and the year are all related to astronomical cycles. By contrast, the seven-day week is an artificial man-made cycle. As Saha says:

> The need for having this short cycle arose out of the psychological need of mankind for having a day of rest and religious service after protracted labour extending over days. The seven-day week with a sabbatical day at the end, or something similar to it, is needed not only by God Almighty, but also by humbler toiling men.

However, there was no unanimity of practice. Whereas the Egyptians had a ten-day week, Vedic Indians had a six-day week. Ancient Iranians had a separate name for each day of the month, but some days, at intervals of approximately seven, were marked out as Din-i-Parvan for religious practice.

The seven-day week as we currently use appears to have come from the Chaldeans, the number seven being chosen for astrological reasons. The Chaldeans were quite advanced in astronomy but somehow they began to link astronomy with astrology. The Chaldeans had seven Gods whom they identified with the Sun, the Moon, Saturn, Jupiter, Mars, Venus and Mercury. According to the Chaldeans, these seven Gods took turns in watching over the world, each God doing duty for one hour at a time. The Chaldeans had 24 hours in the day. Let us label the Gods G_1, G_2, ..., G_7. Then the watch duty would go as follows:

Hour:	1	2	3	4	5	6	7	8	...	23	24
God:	G_1	G_2	G_3	G_4	G_5	G_6	G_7	G_1	...	G_2	G_3

This means that during the first hour on day 2, God G_4 would do duty; and so on. It is easy to see that it would take seven days for the cycle of duty to repeat — see also Fig.7.2.

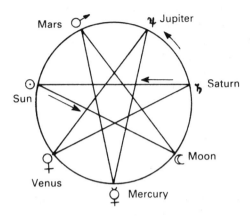

Fig.7.2 According to the Chaldeans, there were seven Gods. They kept watch round the clock taking turns, each God doing one-hour duty. On Sunday, the first hour was always by the Sun God. On Monday, the first hour was by the Moon God. On Tuesday, the first hour was by Mars, and so on. This sequence can be understood if one remembers that the Gods roster runs as: Sun, Venus, Mercury, Moon, Saturn, Jupiter, Mars, Sun, Venus, ... If you start say on Saturday, remember the first hour duty is by Saturn, followed by Jupiter, Mars, etc., then the first- hour duty on Sunday automatically falls to the Sun God and so on. (Notice that the association of celestial bodies to planets closely follows Hindu practice.) The above figure is a chart which depicts this formula in a pictorial form. The arrows along chords indicate who does first-hour duty each day of the week.

The seven-day week came into general use only after the first century AD In fact, according to Saha (and he certainly knew his Bible!), there is no mention in the New Testament about the week day on which Christ was crucified or the day he ascended to Heaven. He adds:

> The fixing of Friday and Sunday for these incidents is a later concoction dating from the fifth century after Christ. All that the New Testament books say is that He was crucified on the first day before the Hebrew festival of Passover ...

So far I have not touched upon the lunar calendar, and that has a fascinating history of its own. As mentioned earlier, the ancients in many lands had observed that the Moon had its own periodicity. They also discovered that if they considered the Moon alone and tried to form years, there was a clash with the recurrence of seasons which were clearly related to the Sun. And thus began the complex process of what might be called luni–solar adjustments. More about that later, but first we shall consider the purely lunar calendar.

The purely lunar calendar was first followed by the ancient Jews. Later, Mohammedans also followed the lunar calendar. In this the year consists of 12 lunar months, the beginning of each month being determined by the first observation of the crescent moon in the evening sky. The months accordingly have 29 or 30 days and the year likewise has 354 or 355 days. The new-year day of the Mohammedan calendar thus retrogrades through the seasons and completes the cycle in about 32 1/2 solar years. The Islamic calendar came into vogue at the time of the death of Prophet Mohammed (AD 632), and the era of the calendar, i.e., *Hejira* was started from AD 622

It is said that the purely lunar calendar was introduced by the Prophet to release the common man from dependence on the priest. Be that as it may, the clash between the lunar calendar and the occurrence of seasons did pose social problems. As a result, Melik Shah of Iran introduced a solar calendar for Iran in AD 1079, and Akbar did likewise in India in AD 1584 under the name of Tarikh Ilahi.

Most ancient civilizations came to terms with the fact that they needed both the lunar as well as the solar clock. And thus came into existence the business of luni–solar adjustments. Many experimented with it — the Chaldeans, the Greeks, the Jews and so on. Obviously we can't discuss all that here but perhaps you have been wondering what our own ancients were up to! Maybe I should now tell you something about what happened in India.

By the way, you are also probably wondering wherefrom I have dug out all the information given in this chapter; largely from the writings of Saha. He wrote several times on the need for calendar reform and in some of his writings, he went into the history of the calendar to show how mankind has been wrestling with this problem for ages. I must call particular attention to a bulky but scholarly report he produced (along with N.C. Lahiri) in 1952. One glance through this report is enough to show how much background reading Saha must have done and how many original books and manuscripts he must have consulted.

Indian civilization is of hoary antiquity and as far as calendar development is concerned, three periods can be recognized.

1. The *Vedic* period from unknown times to 1350 BC.
2. The *Vedanga Jyotish* period from 1350 BC to 400 AD.
3. The *Siddhanta Jyotish* period from 400 AD to modern times.

I am here enumerating only the Hindu calendars; Islamic and Christian calendars (besides Jewish and Parsi calendars) are also to be found in the country but these we have already discussed. Two cardinal principles observed in Hindu calendars are:

1. Religious festivals / observances must take place in the right seasons.
2. Within the proper seasons, the date should be fixed by the phases of the Moon.

As you can see, a luni–solar adjustment is involved. We shall skip the first two periods and go straight to the third, since all the Indian calendars used at present are derived from this third period. Many treatises appear to have been written during this period, the definitive one being *Surya Siddhanta*. As Saha says, this volume lays down the rules for a purely solar calendar which "serve as door posts to which the lunar calendar is hinged like the door".

At the present time, Hindus use almanacs known as *Panchang*. The literal meaning of *Panchang* is five limbs, this term being used since the almanac gives for every day of the year five astrological elements. In addition, the *Panchang* also states when the solar month commences. The five elements are:

1. *Vaara* or the name of the weekday.
2. *Tithi* or the lunar day.
3. *Karan* or half *Tithi*.
4. *Nakshatra* or the lunar asterism in which the Moon is found on the day concerned.
5. *Yoga* or the time-period in which the Sun and Moon move by 13 1/3°.

Saha made an exhaustive study of all this and the variants in the *Panchangs*, nomenclatures, etc., used in the different parts of the country. Obviously I can't go into all of it here but two observations of his merit attention.

Firstly he notes that compared to many other lands, calendar science was slow to take roots in India. Why? Saha puts it as follows:

> The Indians of 300 BC to 400 AD were quite vigorous in body as well as intellect as is shown by their capacity to resist successive hordes of foreign invaders, and their remarkable contributions to religion, art, literature and certain sciences. Why did they not accept the fundamentals of Greek astronomy for calendar calculations earlier?

Saha has himself answered this question. His answer is that firstly, "Greeks of Alexander's time had almost nothing to give to the Indians in calendaric astronomy, for their own knowledge of astronomy at this period was extremely crude." In this respect, the Chaldeans were much better. Chaldean astronomy had by then become a handmaiden for astrology and according to Saha, "Indian thought during these years was definitely hostile to astronomy." Saha quotes from the Buddha to substantiate his point of view. He adds:

> The attitude to astrology and astrolatry on the part of Indian leaders of thought during the period 500 BC to 100 AD was undoubtedly a correct one, and would be welcomed by rationalists of all ages and countries. But such ideas had apparently a very deterrent effect on the study of astronomy in India. Pursuit of astronomical knowledge was confused with astrology, and its cultivation was definitely forbidden in the thousands of monasteries which sprang up all over the country within a few hundred years of the *Nirvaana* (544 BC / 483 BC). Yet monasteries were exactly the place where astronomical studies could be quietly pursued and monks were, on account of their leisure and temperament, eminently fitted for taking up such studies as happened later in Europe, where some of the most eminent astronomers came from the monkist ranks, e.g., Copernicus and Fabricius.
>
> Neither did Hindu leaders opposed to Buddhism encourage astrology and astrolatry. The practical politician thought that the practice of astrology was not conducive to the exercise of personal initiative and condemned it in no uncertain terms. In the *Arthashastra* of *Kautilya*, the following passage is found:

> The objective eludes the foolish man who enquires too much from the stars.

It took a few centuries for such opposition to die down and that is when treatises like *Surya Siddhanta* appeared.

So much for Saha's first point. Coming to the second, due to improper adjustments, etc., all kinds of errors have crept in during the passage of time. Saha thus observes:

> The *Tithi* current for a locality on any day may not be current for another locality. In other words, calculations of the auspicious days which may be correct for one locality may be incorrect for another. If the *Sastras* are to be literally interpreted, every place must have its local calendar.

In short, Saha is vehemently critical of pandits and astrologers clinging on to ancient almanacs, even though they are inaccurate. However, he recognizes that people do need almanacs and would continue to use them for religious as well as other purposes. Granting this, he proposes an All-India Calendar/Almanac in which all calculations would be made scientifically and according to currently accepted principles. Further, one select spot in central India would be identified (like Greenwich in England), and "all calendar calculations should be made for this Indian Greenwich ...". In essence, he wants that all "astrological elements given in the *Panchangs* be abandoned and the calendar made simpler and applicable to all parts of India."

This takes care of the almanacs that guide our social and religious observances. What about the Gregorian calendar that governs official life? He is critical of that too. He says:

Its only merit is that it gives the year length correctly. Its defects are:

1. The months vary in length ...
2. The year and month may fall on any day of the week and this causes inconvenience.
3. The year beginning on Jan. 1 has no correspondence to the cardinal points of the year ... .

There are several other defects which Saha points out but they need not concern us. Is there any way out? And the answer is: Yes, but only a partial one. What it means is that one can certainly have a calendar that is "balanced, regular and perpetual", as would become clear shortly. Such a calendar would certainly eliminate most if not all the problems that the Gregorian calendar causes with respect to *civic* life. For example, our Independence Day would fall every year on the same day of the week. But when it comes to *religious* life there still would be problems because they are determined by the lunar calendar. So we would have to lead a double life guided by two types of calendars as it were; the saving grace is that as far as civic life is concerned, there is an order and predictability (and therefore also boredom?!).

What kind of a scheme does one have in this so-called balanced calendar? Actually people have been trying to invent such a calendar for over a hundred years and several schemes have been suggested. The most popular is the one proposed in 1887 by a person named Armelin. It is actively supported by the World Calendar Reform League with its headquarters in New York. This body has been tirelessly campaigning for the adoption of Armelin's calendar, first with the League of Nations (this was during the period between the two world wars), and subsequently with the UN (after the Second World War). Armelin's calendar is shown in Fig.7.3.

The World Calendar
Balanced, Regular, Perpetual

First quarter

January								February							March						

January								February							March						
S	M	T	W	T	F	S	S	M	T	W	T	F	S	S	M	T	W	T	F	S	
1	2	3	4	5	6	7			1	2	3	4							1	2	
8	9	10	11	12	13	14	5	6	7	8	9	10	11	3	4	5	6	7	8	9	
15	16	17	18	19	20	21	12	13	14	15	16	17	18	10	11	12	13	14	15	16	
22	23	24	25	26	27	28	19	20	21	22	23	24	25	17	18	19	20	21	22	23	
29	30	31					26	27	28	29	30			24	25	26	27	28	29	30	

Second quarter

April								May							June						
S	M	T	W	T	F	S	S	M	T	W	T	F	S	S	M	T	W	T	F	S	
1	2	3	4	5	6	7			1	2	3	4							1	2	
8	9	10	11	12	13	14	5	6	7	8	9	10	11	3	4	5	6	7	8	9	
15	16	17	18	19	20	21	12	13	14	15	16	17	18	10	11	12	13	14	15	16	
22	23	24	25	26	27	28	19	20	21	22	23	24	25	17	18	19	20	21	22	23	
29	30	31					26	27	28	29	30			24	25	26	27	28	29	30 ** W	

Third quarter

July								August							September						
S	M	T	W	T	F	S	S	M	T	W	T	F	S	S	M	T	W	T	F	S	
1	2	3	4	5	6	7			1	2	3	4							1	2	
8	9	10	11	12	13	14	5	6	7	8	9	10	11	3	4	5	6	7	8	9	
15	16	17	18	19	20	21	12	13	14	15	16	17	18	10	11	12	13	14	15	16	
22	23	24	25	26	27	28	19	20	21	22	23	24	25	17	18	19	20	21	22	23	
29	30	31					26	27	28	29	30			24	25	26	27	28	29	30	

Fourth quarter

October								November							December						
S	M	T	W	T	F	S	S	M	T	W	T	F	S	S	M	T	W	T	F	S	
1	2	3	4	5	6	7			1	2	3	4							1	2	
8	9	10	11	12	13	14	5	6	7	8	9	10	11	3	4	5	6	7	8	9	
15	16	17	18	19	20	21	12	13	14	15	16	17	18	10	11	12	13	14	15	16	
22	23	24	25	26	27	28	19	20	21	22	23	24	25	17	18	19	20	21	22	23	
29	30	31					26	27	28	29	30			24	25	26	27	28	29	30 * W	

*Worldsday, (a World Holiday), W or 31 December (365th day), follows 30 December every year.
**The Leapyear Day, (another World Holiday), W or 31 June follows 30 June in leap years.

Fig.7.3 The world calendar

Its features are:

1. Every year is the same.
2. The year is divided into four quarters; all the four are identical.
3. Each quarter contains exactly three months, 13 weeks and 91 days.

4. Each quarter begins on a Sunday and ends on a Saturday. If Saturday and Sunday are taken as weekend holidays, then each month would have exactly 26 week days.
5. In order to make the calendar perpetual, at the same time retaining astronomical accuracy, the 365th day of the year is called *Year End Day*. In a leap year, there will be in addition a *Year Middle Day*.

The calendar is quite simple, isn't it? Some of you may even be able to get it by heart!

No proposal, however good it might be, is free from opposition and the World Calendar Plan is no exception. Objections have been raised mainly by Jewish organisations on the ground that the Plan interferes with the unbroken seven-day week by introducing World Day and Leap Year Day without any week-day denomination (i.e., these special days have no names like Sunday, Monday, etc.). This, the Jewish groups say, will interfere with their religious life. In a speech delivered before one of the UN Committees in 1953, Saha patiently argued that the seven-day week was not all that sacrosanct as it was claimed to be. Winding up his arguments he said:

> The religious sanction for the seven-day cycle is therefore either non-existent or slight amongst communities other than Jews, and even amongst them, it is not very ancient ... It would be egoistical on the part of a particular community or communities to try to impede the passage of a measure of such great usefulness to the whole of mankind ... Calendars are based on Science, which everybody must bow to; and on *Convention* which may be altered by mutual consent...
>
> Let us follow the wise Chinese maxim: *Religions are many but Reason is one.* World harmony can be promoted only by sweet reasonableness.

Any chance of such reasonableness at least in the next century?

Appendix to Chapter 7

Perhaps you have been puzzled by some of the technical details in this chapter. Maybe this Appendix will help you. When we stand out in the open and gaze at the sky, we see a vast canopy. During the day it is the Sun which dominates while at night the Moon and the stars take over (assuming that there are no clouds). From ancient times people have been observing celestial objects, and to indicate their positions three kinds of coordinate systems have been evolved namely, the horizon system, the equatorial system and the galactic system. Of these, we shall be interested only in the second; nevertheless, a brief digression on the horizon system is useful.

This system is illustrated in Fig.(a). Essentially, we imagine we are in a flat terrain. Directly above is the zenith while the horizon is at infinite distance at ground level. The position of any object in the sky is described in terms of the angles shown.

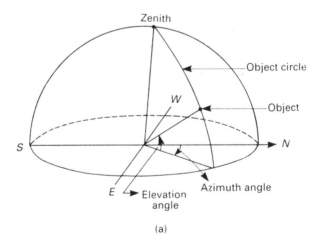

(a)

The equatorial system is shown in Fig.(b). Here we imagine concentric with the Earth a huge sphere called the celestial sphere. We imagine that celestial objects (e.g., the Sun) move on the surface of this sphere. The celestial equator is concentric with the geographic equator and the celestial North Pole is directly above the geographic North Pole. The Pole Star is at the celestial north pole (to within 45' of arc).

Suppose there is an object at position A on the celestial sphere. To describe its position, we first draw the celestial latitude and longitude passing through A. Say there is an observer on Earth at Q. The point on the celestial sphere directly above him is the zenith, and is shown as Z. Draw the longitude passing through Z. Two angles can now be defined as shown in Fig.(b), and these two angles fix the position of A for the observer at Q. Of these two angles, the *declination* δ (which is nothing but the celestial latitude of position A) is given (as usual) in degrees, but the other angle called the *hour angle* is given in hours! There is of course a reason and this would be clear soon.

Next we consider the Earth and the Sun. The Earth moves in an elliptic orbit with a mean Earth-Sun distance of 1.496×10^{11}m — see Fig.(c). The rotational axis of the Earth is tilted with respect to

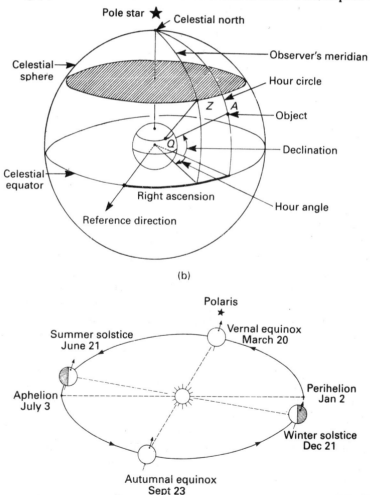

(b)

(c)

the orbital plane by 23.45°. As already remarked, the rotation of the Earth about its axis leads to the day–night phenomenon and the motion of the Earth around the Sun produces the seasons. The position of the Sun in the celestial sphere may be indicated using the equatorial system, as shown in Fig.(d). Observe that the rays from the Sun to the Earth are parallel to the plane containing the hour circle.

ϕ: Latitude of Q $\quad\quad$ Q: Position of observer on Earth
δ: Declination of Sun $\quad$ H: Horizon of Q
$\quad\quad\quad\quad\quad\quad\quad\quad\quad$ Z: Zenith of Q

(d)

Four positions in the Earth's orbit around the Sun are of special importance — see Fig.(c). These are the two equinoxes (Vernal and Autumnal) and the solstices (summer and winter). The significance of these events may be better appreciated from Fig.(e). For convenience, the Sun's rays are depicted horizontal. Since the angle between the polar axis of the Earth and the Sun's rays changes with the seasons, it appears in Fig.(e) as if the axis rocks or wobbles. Actually the axis does not wobble with respect to the celestial pole; it only *appears* to, relative to the Sun. But this apparent wobble has important consequences and in fact the occurrence of seasons has a lot to do with it. In Fig.(e(i)), the Sun is directly over the Tropic of Cancer (latitude = 23.45°N). This happens on June 21 and thus an observer at latitude 23.45° would see the Sun directly overhead (i.e., at the zenith) at noon. On Autumnal Equinox, the Sun is directly over the equator, having travelled "down" between June 21 and September 23 — see Fig.(e(ii)). Continuing its downward journey, the Sun reaches the Tropic of Capricorn (latitude = 23.45°S) on Winter Solstice day, i.e., December 21 — see Fig.(e(iii)). The Sun now begins its northern journey and reaches the equator on Vernal Equinox day, i.e., March 20 — see Fig.(e(iv)).

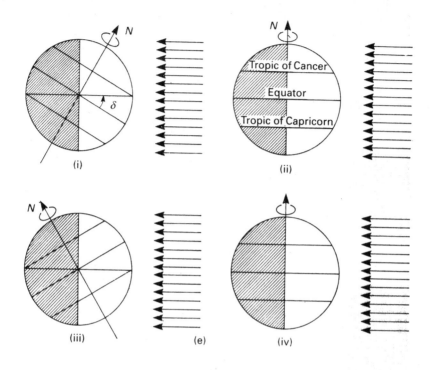

(i)

(ii)

(iii)

(e)

(iv)

We know of course the Sun does not actually go up and down as Fig.(e) might suggest. What really happens is that as the Earth goes round the Sun, the declination angle δ varies — see Fig.(f) — and this is what is illustrated in Fig.(e); and this is what leads to the seasons. For example, when the Sun is over the Tropic of Cancer, no sunlight reaches the South Pole — it is dark there all 24 hours and a person living there (many scientists do!) does not experience day and night in the sense we normally do. On the other hand, for a person on the North Pole, the Sun never sets! Actually one doesn't have to go as far as the North Pole; there are places in northern Norway where the Sun does not set on June 21. This region is called the Land of the Midnight Sun, and tourists flock there on Summer Solstice day to witness the spectacle of the Sun being around all 24 hours. In slightly lower latitudes, the Sun does rise and set but the days sure are long in summer; the Sun can rise as early as 3:30 a.m. and set only around 10:30 p.m. Therefore people use thick curtains so that they can shut out sunlight and go to sleep! Of course, in winter it is the other way around and it is now the turn of people in the southern hemisphere to enjoy long days. Fig.(g) gives an indication of how the Sun appears to move on the celestial sphere for an observer Q in the northern hemisphere.

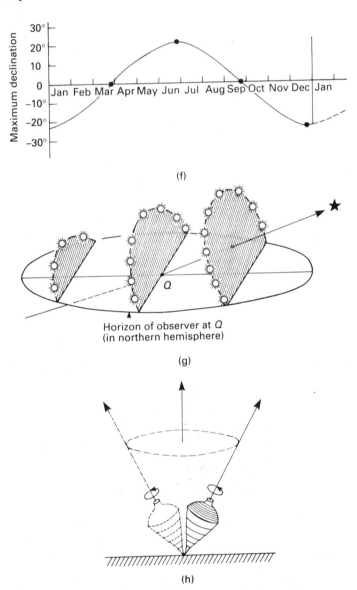

(f)

Horizon of observer at Q
(in northern hemisphere)

(g)

(h)

The celestial sphere is useful not only for tracking the Sun but also the stars. In this connection, we need a reference direction.

Now to locate points on the surface of the Earth we use the latitude and the longitude. The latitude gets defined automatically but for the longitude we need a reference. By common consent, 0° longitude is taken to be the meridian through Greenwich in England. The point with 0° latitude and 0° longitude is unique, and provides an origin of coordinates. On the celestial sphere, we can readily define the celestial equator. But which point on this equator do we take as the reference? If such a point is identified, then the line joining the centre of the Earth to this point O, say, becomes the reference direction.

This reference direction is defined as follows: On March 21, the declination δ becomes zero and the Sun is over the equator. If now we consult the graph in Fig.(f), we will notice that δ becomes identically equal to zero at one instant of time on March 21. It is not as if the Sun is *exactly* over the equator *throughout the day*; it is no doubt very very close but it is exactly over the equator only at one *particular* instant. The position of the Sun on the celestial sphere at *that* instant provides the reference.

At night, the stars replace the Sun in the sky and we will see, among other things, various constellations. Thousands of years ago, the constellation that was seen along the reference direction on Vernal Equinox day was Aries. But in course of time this has changed because the Earth is like a spinning top and as you know a spinning top precesses — see Fig.(h). As a result, some other constellation (Pisces) now appears in the reference direction. However, as a tribute to ancients who had studied some of these matters, the reference direction is sometimes referred to as the first direction of Aries.

8 *River Physics*

8.1 Introduction

I am sure the title of this chapter must be puzzling. River physics is not a common term and you might even wonder what has physics got to do with rivers (see Box 8.1). The best way of clearing your doubt is to tell you about Saha's interest in rivers.

Supposing you ask a present-day theoretical physicist: "What do you understand by the term river physics?" He would probably reply, "You must be kidding — there is no such term." Change your tactics and ask: "Do rivers flow just like that or is there any physics involved anywhere?" This time he might say: "Sure there is some underlying physics; gravity, gradient, hydrodynamics and boring stuff like that." It would now be his turn to ask a question and he would probably mutter: "But why are you bothered about such dull and mundane things? There are better things to do in physics, you know."

Yes there always are but somebody *has* to bother about rivers and it had better be someone knowledgeable; who better than a sound physicist?

Now you might ask why at all should anyone bother about rivers. Isn't it true, like in the famous Negro spiritual: "Old Man river, he just keeps on rollin, rollin along ..." ? No sir, one has to bother, on account of a number of reasons like floods, for example. You would probably argue that floods are an act of God — they usually are but man also can be responsible for them by his foolish acts.

Box 8.1 Here is one small example of how physics is connected with rivers. Consider a river in the northern hemisphere and say it flows north as in Fig.(a). Due to the rotation of the Earth there is a force $\vec{F}$ called the Coriolis force (try to find out what it is). The velocity vector $\vec{v}$, the angular velocity $\vec{\omega}$ and $\vec{F}$ have relative orientations as shown in Fig.(a). Thanks to the Coriolis force, the water is pushed somewhat towards the east (see Fig.(b)), and as a result the right bank of the river tends to get more eroded.

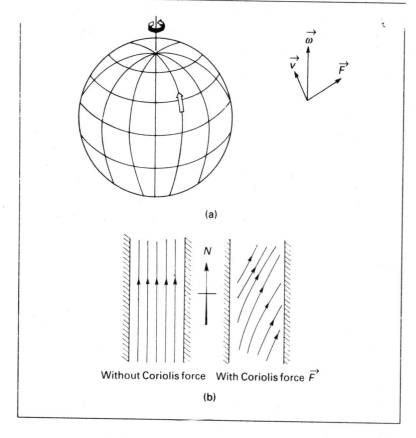

(a)

Without Coriolis force   With Coriolis force $\vec{F}$

(b)

Indeed it was a disastrous flood caused by human thoughtlessness and insensitivity that made Saha become deeply interested in the problem of rivers.

8.2 The Great Flood of 1922

In a sense, Saha's concern for floods and rivers actually goes back to his boyhood days. He came from a village where floods were a part of life and often he had to row back and forth to school. In 1922 there was a disastrous flood in Northern Bengal and Saha's revered teacher Acharya P.C. Ray was active in flood relief. Saha says that Ray was so much immersed in flood-relief work that Mahatma Gandhi used to jocularly refer to him (Ray) as the "Doctor of Floods". Many came to the assistance of Ray and this included Subhas Chandra Bose and Meghnad Saha. The latter was given charge of publicity, i.e., arousing public opinion to the need for

relief, etc. Saha went much further to analyse the cause of the
floods and came up with a brilliant article in the scholarly journal
The Modern Review. Saha begins by remarking:

> It has been said that Bengal is the "gift of the Ganges (and of
> Brahmaputra)". But along with gifts, not infrequently, come curses...

What Saha means is floods.

Bengal is the meeting place of the two great rivers, the Ganges
and the Brahmaputra. If you study the atlas carefully, you will
realise that this meeting is quite remarkable. They both originate
in the upper Himalayas, flow for a while in opposite directions,
then reverse and finally rush towards each other to unite barely
a few tens of kilometres from the sea. Saha has given a graphic
description of the river system of (the then) Bengal (dominated of
course by these two mighty rivers) but it is not necessary for us to
go into all that. What we need to know as far as the flood of 1922
is concerned is that there is a river named Atrai which rises in
northern Bengal, works its way down from NNW to SSE, and joins
the Brahmaputra about 70 km or so before the latter mingles with
the Ganges. The lower course of Atrai passes through low-lying
territory which remains under 1–2 metres of water for close to five
months in a year. Saha remarks:

> From the very nature of this tract, it is subject to annual seasonal
> flooding ... these annual inundations, instead of being a source of
> mischief, are of the greatest possible benefit as they fertilise the
> soil by precipitation of river-borne silt and render artificial irrigation
> unnecessary.

In this region they grow a variety of paddy called *aman* which
has a rather long stem, almost four metres. The paddy is sown
before the onset of rains and the growth of the paddy plant keeps
pace with the rise of water during the rainy season, *provided the
rise is gradual.*

The upper reaches of Atrai are not so much water logged as the
lower regions are, being comparatively higher. Normally, this region
receives about 170 cm of rain a year of which 35 cm is precipitated
in September. But in September 1922, there was a downpour of
over 60 cm in the short span of six consecutive days, and that spelt
real trouble.

Downpours like this though rare were not totally unknown, and
there was earlier in 1871 a similar deluge. But this time there was
one major difference and that caused all the havoc. Believe it or
not, it was the railways! I am sure you would think I am out of

my mind but, as Saha says, "to understand the nature of the havoc done, one must have a look at the railway lines in the district."

I have given in Fig.8.1(b) a simplified version of the railway map pertinent to our discussion. (I should add that the region shown

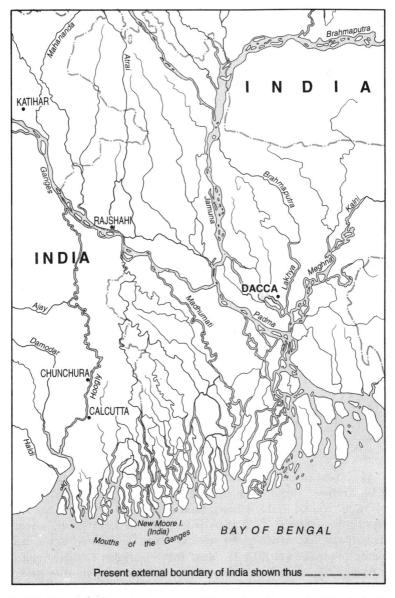

Fig.8.1 Rivers of Bengal (most of this region is now in Bangladesh). (a) shows a general map.

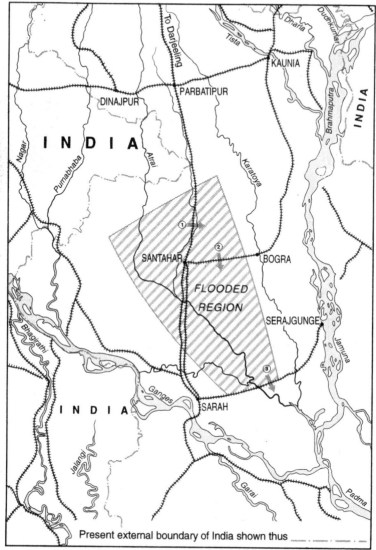

Fig.8.1 *continued* (b) is a simplified map of the region relevant to us. Prior to the coming of the railways, flood waters used to drain to the sea following the terrain gradient which is from NW to SE. With the advent of the railways, the embankments acted as "dams" and caused widespread flooding. In the flood of 1922, the "dam" first breached at 1. Water rushing out flooded the downstream region till breach 2 eased the situation there. The water then spread further down again, causing a flood till breach 3 provided some relief. In this way, the flood waters cascaded and spread in steps to cause havoc over a vast region.

formed a part of what was then called East Bengal. Today, it is in Bangladesh.) Basically there were, at that time, three tracks: (i) A South–North track originating at Sara and going via Santahar to Parbatipur and further on to Darjeeling, (ii) a West–East line from Sara to Serajgunge and (iii) a similar West–East line from Santahar to Bogra. The Sara–Santahar section had actually two tracks side by side, a broad gauge and a metre gauge. What has all this got to do with floods? Patience!

The railway tracks were laid on an embankment which essentially acted like a great big wall. Here and there a few bridges and culverts were introduced to accommodate the streams and rivulets that came in the way, but barring those, it was one long stretch of wall about 2 metres high all the way.

Let us now turn to the extraordinary downpour that occurred in the third week of September 1922. Normally the rain water was carried by Atrai (flowing NW to SE) but this time the water was just too much and so it spread sideways causing extensive flooding. Sad, but not an unknown phenomenon and such flooding *had* occasionally occurred in the past. But there is one thing about flood water; unless trapped, it does not stick around; rather, it follows the gradient and drains away. Maybe sometimes the drainage might be slow, but water always flows down — unless there is something to obstruct it. And in 1922 there was namely, the double track from Sara to Santahar. Saha describes what actually happened:

> The western half of the flood-water, from Dinajpore, spread over the Atrai basin, comprising the whole of the Naogaon subdivision. But it could not breach the railway line which acted as a double dam [due to the presence of two parallel tracks, the broad gauge and the metre gauge] across this volume of moving water. The only way of escape was through the channel of the Atrai and some other small rivers which under such exceptional circumstances could discharge only a small fraction of the water accumulated behind it. This line is again very insufficiently provided with culverts, and oftentimes the culverts of the metre gauge line have no corresponding culvert on the parallel broad gauge section ...
>
> The flood-water being held back effectively began to rise in level and extend further over the district. People looked with dismay on the boiling sheet of water beneath them which seemed likely to swallow everything ... They soon saw their paddy fields, their homesteads, being submerged under water. They were driven to take shelter on high grounds, on trees, on boats ... The water-level continued to rise till ... the difference of level on the west and on the east side amounted to four to five feet [~ 1.6 metres] — a clear indication

that the railway line was blocking the free passage of water ... *thanks to the railway embankments, the water took a pretty long time in subsiding.*

Old timers to whom Saha and others talked said that they had previously experienced equally heavy downpours but not *sustained* flooding. Before the railways came, the rivers would surely overflow and cause flooding but on account of the natural gradient the flood waters would drain away. This time there was a manmade obstruction to the drainage and owing to continued stagnation the rice crop was totally destroyed. So the real problem was that the people who built the railways did not think about water drainage and provide a sufficient number of openings in the otherwise uninterrupted "wall". Apparently, when the broad gauge track was laid on the side of the metre gauge track, they made matters worse by *reducing some of the existing bridges on the metre-gauge line to half or one-third their original length!*

Thanks to the dam "donated" by the railways, flood waters began to accumulate and spread far, including to regions not normally blessed with heavy rains. Ultimately, even the railway tracks could not hold and a breach occurred — see breach 1 in Fig.8.1(b). And now the flood spread to Bogra. Once again the waters faced a dam in the shape of the Santahar–Bogra track. Fortunately, this gave way near Adamdighi and about this Saha observes, "People say that but for this breach, they would have drowned like rats." The people of Adamdighi and the neighbourhood were thus saved by this kindly breach — breach 2 in Fig.8.1(b). Liberated by the Adamdighi breach, part of the water now entered the Pabna area where again there was an obstruction in the shape of the Sara–Serajgunge track.

Can one really be sure that it was all the fault of the railways? So Saha goes back to check on old records and this is what he found in the District Gazetteer of Rajshahi of 1871 when also there was a deluge — but no railways! The official record says:

> The waters were out on this occasion from the end of August to the second week of October, and the whole country was flooded. It is believed that these were the highest flood on record in this district; but the damage to the crops was comparatively small. The cattle suffered much from the loss of fodder, and the people were greatly inconvenienced by being driven to seek shelter on high places. When the water subsided, cholera broke out in epidemic form. The *boro aman* rice crop, however, grew on in most places uninjured, and managed to keep its head above waters, even when they rose quickly, and eventually a very fair rice harvest was reaped.

Saha assertively adds:

> The havocs done by the present flood [of 1922] and the flood of
> 1871 are identical in all respects [as far as people in the western
> region were concerned] except as regards the destruction of crops.
> In 1871, the flood was not held up at railway embankments. The
> water rose slowly and subsided rapidly enabling the *aman* crop to
> survive the deluge. But this year, the railway embankments held up
> the water so long, that the crops became a total loss.

The great flood of 1922 was not the first one to be caused
by the railways. Earlier in 1892 there was a serious flood in the
Dinajpore region. By now a railway line had been built there and the
embankments started damming up the water. The District Gazeteer
of Dinajpore records:

> An enquiry into the cause of this disastrous flood led to the conclusion
> that the Railway line which bisects the district from east to west was
> in a large measure responsible for the damage done by holding up
> the flood waters coming up from the north. To obviate this, the
> waterway was greatly increased ...

Net result? "No flood worthy of the name has occurred since."
Saha bitterly complains:

> If the Railway engineers who constructed the Sara–Santahar and
> Sara–Serajgunge Railway were conversant with this episode, and
> cared to take their lesson from it, the people of Rajshahi and Pabna
> would have been spared much of the misery to which they have been
> subjected.

What about the version of the Railway authorities? In their
official communique, they dutifully described the flood and the
damage it had caused to Railway property! Naturally, they gave no
hint that they were the real culprits.

Once again, was Saha dreaming up allegations and inventing a
wild hypothesis? Far from it. Dr. Bentley, the Director of Public Health (an Englishman) went on record at the same time as
follows:

> Unfortunately the engineers who are responsible for the construction
> of the District Board Roads and Railway Lines in this region did not
> trouble their heads about the natural drainage of the country. The
> roads and railway lines are insufficiently provided with culverts and
> waterways. The water in itself is not an evil but it must be quickly
> drained off.

Thanks to stagnation there was later a malaria epidemic and that is what bothered Bentley. He did not stop with this but went on to describe experiments on water drainage carried out by a friend of his, how culverts judiciously inserted would let flood waters pass on to the fields where it is needed for crops, etc. Saha concludes by asking:

> Is it [the flood of 1922] to be considered wholly as an Act of God, or has the Hand of Man any share ... ?

After an impartial enquiry he is forced to say that man must have a fairly large share of the blame. Saha adds:

> I do not for a moment suggest that the railway engineers have purposely done the mischief. But it is clear they have failed to do good, or did not care to study the interest of the people ... It is difficult for an engineer trained in England to realise the immense importance of unobstructed flow of water to the peasant here. The peasant of Bengal has no railway shares to live upon ... He lives and dies with his paddy fields.

The article written by Saha in the *Modern Review* was mainly intended to inform the public and in writing it, he was partially discharging his duties as the Publicity Officer. But this indepth study of the flood of 1922 also appears to have got Saha deeply interested in the general problem of rivers and how to manage them. And that is where river physics really enters the picture.

8.3 Rivers and civilizations

After 1922, Saha witnessed three major floods, i.e., in 1931, 1935 and 1943. Elsewhere, science was being applied not only for improving standards of living but also for the control of rivers. Saha therefore made a deep study of the problem and whenever the opportunity arose, expressed himself forcefully. In fact he made *The Problem of Indian Rivers* the theme of his Presidential Address to the National Institute of Sciences in 1935.

Without water life is impossible. This lesson was known from very ancient times and, as Saha puts it,

> Human civilisation on this globe of ours has, since time immemorial, chiefly centred about rivers and river basins. Who can conceive of Egypt without the Nile, of ancient Sumer and Babylon without the Tigris and the Euphrates, and of China without the Hoang Ho (the

Yellow River) and the Yangtsekiang? The early growth of settled human life in river basins is to be ascribed to the fact that rivers supplied the largest amount of needs of early societies ...

One might argue: "What about the Greek and the Roman civilizations? They were both maritime civilizations, the former centred around the Aegean Sea and the latter around the Mediterranean." True. But, as Saha points out, both these were in fact clearing houses for products generated in neighbourhood riparian tracts.

8.4 Rivers and irrigation

River valley civilizations came into existence only after man had discovered and mastered agriculture. Agriculture needs water, and rivers supplied water. However, it did require some effort to tap that water and divert it to the fields. And this is how the art of irrigation came into existence. Saha says, "Irrigation in different ways was practised on a stupendous scale in Egypt, Babylon, old China, as well as in India." However, all this required some study and observation of the behaviour of rivers. Egypt, for example, is often described as the gift of the Nile. Ancient Egyptians observed the river carefully and discovered a cyclic rhythm — there were seasons when the river was in flood and overflowed its banks and there were periods when the river was almost dry (we discussed this in an earlier chapter). They then realised that by suitable manipulations "the rivers could be made to do more good than if they were left to themselves." This is what irrigation is basically all about.

Saha applauds the great success achieved by ancient Mesopotamians in agriculture and says:

In Mesopotamia [today's Iraq], the two rivers [Euphrates and the Tigris] run through a desert country and only a small fringe of land, on either side of each river, is directly accessible to the river water. But the ancient dwellers of the land, the Sumerians, five thousand years ago, cut canals from the rivers and irrigated their fields. In fact, but for the network of irrigation canals with which the whole land was intersected, very little of the country would have been habitable. Elaborate precautions were taken by the State for maintaining the canal system from the attack of external enemies and from the harmful effect of internal quarrels. This magnificent canal system was the cause of the great prosperity of ancient Iraq, upto 1258 AD, when the Mongols under Hulagu Khan conquered the country and systematically destroyed the canal system by blocking the mouth of canals and allowing them to fall into decay. Iraq ... has never recovered from this catastrophe.

8.5 Irrigation in ancient India

Compared to Egypt or Mesopotamia, India is very much bigger, and there are several river systems, each with its own peculiarity. Accordingly, irrigation practices also were (and continue to be) somewhat diversified. Saha describes them for us:

Here [i.e., Punjab], in ancient times, water was tapped by canals which were cut off from the banks of rivers. The canals were filled with water only during floods. The western part of the Ganges valley does not suffer so much from defect of rainfall, but there are wide tracts in this part which are far away from the banks of the main rivers, and from which rain water drains off quickly. The problem is to bring water to these areas by means of perennial canals. Southern India again presents a different aspect. In the centre it is a tableland, and the rain, which falls mostly within a short period, drains off quickly to the eastern sea. Ancient rulers held up the water by throwing dams across convenient sites thus creating reservoirs and artificial lakes from which water could be tapped for agricultural purpose whenever necessary. This is sometimes known as storage or tank irrigation ... Southern India is full of huge storage tanks used for irrigation which testify to the ancient rulers' solicitude ...

Not all parts of southern India are served by tanks, the Cauvery delta being the prime example. Saha has an interesting theory about how this delta came into existence, a theory which actually was advanced by Sir William Willcocks, the builder of the famed Aswan Dam in Egypt. Sir William was invited by the Calcutta University (at Saha's instance?) to deliver lectures on rivers and how to tame them. Drawing upon those lectures Saha says that (according to Sir William):

The branches of the Ganges in the Bengal delta were originally a system of canals dug by some ancient king for affording a quick outlet for the Ganges water to the seas. This not only prevented catastrophic floods, but allowed silt-laden water to be distributed over a wide area adding fertility to the soil. Further, it had a healthy flushing action over the whole countryside, clearing all stagnant pools which are the hotbeds of malaria and other diseases.

Not only did Sir William declare that the fan-shaped delta of the Ganges was the work of man in some pre-Christian era, but he went on to suggest that the Cauvery delta too was the handiwork of man, actually settlers from Bengal!! About this Saha writes:

This coincidence [i.e., similarity of canal system in the Gangetic delta and the Cauvery delta], according to him [Sir William] is not fortuitous but must have been due to immigrants from Bengal who carried with them the knowledge of the irrigation of the Damodar area to South India before the Christian era. The theory is not improbable in the light of what we know of historical events of those periods.

Saha points out that Tanjore (in the Cauvery delta) and Burdwan (in the Gangetic delta) were, in 1815, two of the richest districts in India, with Burdwan ahead of Tanjore. Then things took a strange turn. In Tanjore, Sir Arthur Cotton "courageously undertook to restore the old anicut [dam] across the Cauvery erected by old Hindu Kings, and distribute the waters evenly in the delta." The opposite process was undertaken by engineers in Burdwan. Driven by the need to lay roads and railway tracks, they interfered with the ancient flushing system. Net result: Water stagnated, malaria became rampant and soil fertility declined. Tanjore now raced way ahead of Burdwan in health and prosperity. Whether one agrees or not as to ancient settlers from Bengal being responsible for the irrigation system in the Cauvery delta, the message coming through clearly is that one must deal with rivers in an integrated manner and after a proper study. As Saha puts it:

The present age is an age of science when the forces of nature are being controlled with an amount of success which could not be dreamt of by early generations.

But this control comes only from a deep and penetrating study of the problem, in this case the problem of rivers. And such studies call for special laboratories, and facilities for data collection — more about all this shortly.

8.6 Some lessons from history

Before considering how exactly to tackle the problem of rivers, it is perhaps useful to draw some lessons from history. Rivers are great forces of Nature and they have their own idiosyncracies. It is necessary therefore to have some knowledge of them.

Let us first glance at a few pages of Roman history. According to an American hydrologist named Freeman (whom Saha quotes), there was in the days of the Roman Empire a bend in the River Tiber — see Fig.8.2 — and this apparently threatened the city of Rome. But there was also a solution, which was to short-circuit the bend by artificial means. However, that was not done. Freeman says:

> Ancient Rome had important river problems. The question of cutting off a river bend in the Tiber, which threatened Rome was gravely discussed by the Senate and dropped for the profound reason that "Nature understood what was best when it formed the river in its present shape."

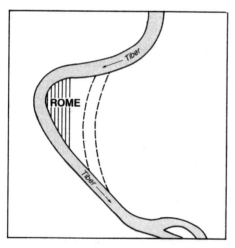

Fig.8.2 This is a schematic of the relative disposition of the river Tiber and the city of Rome. The hatching shows how the flood waters were expected to spread (and in the process affect the city). The dashed lines indicate the solution proposed, which the Roman Senate chose to ignore.

So the Romans sat back and did nothing. Result? According to Saha, "The result was that imperial Rome decayed through outbreaks of malaria." Two thousand years later there was a similar problem which the city of Nuremburg in Germany faced from the river Rhine. Controlled experiments were performed in the lab and a proper means of solving the problem by cutting a cross channel was evolved — this of course was Saha's theme song all along namely, we need similar labs to study the physics of our rivers.

Let us get back again to ancient times, and focus now on the rivers in the Punjab and Sind. (Today Sind and a part of Punjab are in Pakistan but that does not matter; we are here dealing with

geography and not politics). Figure 8.3 gives an idea of the changes
in the Punjab rivers. About this Saha says:

> You will see that the Punjab rivers have a tendency to change their
> course and that they generally move west. There is a fight going on
> between the desert and the river valleys. The desert is constantly
> encroaching on the rivers and pushing them to the North West.

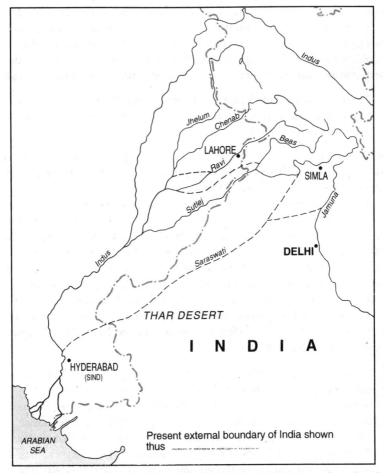

Fig.8.3 This figure (adapted from Saha's Presidential address referred to in
the text) shows the rivers of the (undivided) Punjab and the changes they
have undergone in time. The dashed lines show the ancient flow paths.
River Saraswati (mentioned in Vedic prayers) has vanished! Some streams
which once fed into it now disappear into the desert sands.

How do we know that such large-scale drifts in the river course
have taken place? From archaeological excavations, about which

Saha says:

> Besides Harappa and Mohanjodaro [about which you must undoubt-
> edly be aware], a large number of cities have been found buried
> under the sands of Sind and Rajputana. These cities *could not* have
> existed unless there was more plentiful supply of water in these
> regions 5000 years ago than is to be found now.

What could have been the source of water in these regions? The
belief is that there was another river Saraswati which derived from
the rivers of eastern Punjab and that this river Saraswati flowed
more or less parallel to the Indus, thus making the region in between
very prosperous. And then something happened. According to Saha,

> The lower course of Saraswati ran dry during Vedic times and its
> course is marked by a dry channel. The other rivers have moved
> away generally to the West.

What caused such changes? One doesn't quite know, but Saha
quotes geologists to suggest that probably they were triggered by
crustal movements of the earth.

We now turn to the Ganges–Brahmaputra system. Among the
rivers of the world, the Amazon in Brazil comes first in terms
of volume of water discharged into the sea. Next comes the
Mississipi–Missouri system in America, closely followed by the
Ganges–Brahmaputra. In fact, during the peak of the monsoon,
our rivers beat the Mississipi–Missouri; and they leave the famous
Nile way behind, even though the Nile is much longer.

The Ganges has played much havoc, most devastating of which
was the wiping out of Pataliputra, the seat of the Magadhan Empire.
Describing it, Saha writes:

> Ancient Pataliputra which was the capital city of India from the
> 6th century BC to about the 5th century AD — an interval of
> nearly a thousand years — owed its importance to its position as
> an important trade centre at the junction of five rivers [of which
> the Ganges was the most important] ... It now lies buried under
> the present city of Patna at a depth of about 17 feet [roughly three
> and a half metres] below the ground level. Its destruction was due
> to floods. It appears that in the deltaic regions, the level of a city
> gradually goes down while that of the surrounding country rises, so
> protective bunds have to be constructed to keep the flood water out.
> But sometimes, particularly if the city is between two rivers, as was
> the case with Pataliputra, and there is simultaneous flood in the two
> rivers, these bunds give way ...

That in short was how Pataliputra disappeared (under silt), and with it the Magadhan Empire.

Another city to be wiped out by rivers was Gaur in Bengal. From the fifth century AD to 1576, it was the capital of Eastern India and about it Saha observes:

> It was situated between two branches of the Ganges river, and another large tributary, the Mahananda, flowed nearby. A very unhealthy swamp grew in its rear on account of changes in the river course and, possibly due to the lowering of city level, the drains in the city could not discharge the sewage to the rivers properly. The result was the outbreak of an epidemic which swept away the majority of the population about the year 1575 and the vast city, which was estimated by the Portugese merchants of the 16th century to contain a population of over two millions, now lies buried under an overgrowth of jungle.

Wiping out cities is but one aspect of the havoc caused by the great rivers. Basically they seem to be engaged in a fight with the land and, depending on the circumstances, appear determined to flow as they please. I was most astounded to learn that as recently as two hundred or so years ago, the courses of the Ganges and the Brahmaputra were *quite different* from what they are now. In fact they did not meet, and independently discharged their waters into the sea at two different points separated by as much as 200 km. This is not a cock and bull story; there exist maps made around 1750 by officers of the East India Company to prove this. And then in 1787 there was a great catastrophic flood. So much silt was deposited as a result that it *completely* changed the course of both the Ganges and the Brahmaputra, which now decided to unite before merging into the sea! So you see, big rivers ought to be taken mighty seriously and it is not just a question of building a bridge here or cutting a canal there or even throwing a dam across (as people usually imagine).

8.7 Some sound advice

One of the first to make this last point forcefully was an enlightened Englishman named Sir Francis Spring who had served as the Chief Engineer to the Government of India. In that capacity he had supervised the construction of many bridges, and drawing upon his experience he presented to the Government in 1903 a lucid document entitled *River Training and Control*. In it he said:

Heretofore there has been no pretence of organising any such research in connection with the engineering of the canals and the railways of India. Engineers have gone on blundering, benefiting, rather by chance than by design, by the experience of their predecessors, and each considering himself lucky if he escapes disaster at the tremendous forces of nature — amongst which some of the most potent for good or evil are the great rivers — with which he has to struggle ...

According to Sir Francis, India had then a competent cadre of engineers (true of British origin) as good as scientific engineers of any country in Europe, but the Government of the day was only keen on extracting work and not in supporting original research. Sir Francis cautioned that such stinginess did not at all pay; on the contrary, research could lead to the saving of money on projects. Pleading specifically for a thorough study of Indian rivers, he wrote:

The State ought not to lose sight of the importance of endeavouring, by consistent, logical and well-organised research, to learn something more definite than is now known about the physics of long reaches of rivers.

Thus Saha was not the first to talk about the physics of rivers; Sir Francis had done so as far back as the turn of the century. Then, as now, the Government believed in turning a deaf ear to all sane suggestions. So the poor conscientious field engineer was left to "fight" rivers without having the foggiest notion of how powerful the river was and could be. In desperation Sir Francis exclaims:

It is difficult to avoid the conclusion, ... that for lack of adequate knowledge, the engineers concerned with the interests of the inhabitants of the Indus [Sir Francis is here referring to projects carried out in/Sind on the Indus river] have been obliged to work more or less in the dark in their fight with the river, and to make matters worse it has continuously happened that, owing to the climate, to the exigencies of public service, no sooner does one engineer get some inkling of the tricks than he is replaced by one with all his experiences to gain; and in six months he, in turn, is replaced by somebody else whose experience of the river has been limited to crossing it. *How, under so haphazard a system, anything gets done at all is a marvel!*

How painfully true this last remark is even today, almost a century later and half a century into Independence!

Sir Francis did not stop with complaints; he made positive and detailed recommendations for (i) a River Commission and (ii) a laboratory for the organised study of the physics of the great alluvial rivers. Like it does with all useful reports, the Government must have religiously filed away the report of Sir Francis into one of its dungeons, leaving it to the future historian to dig it out. It is to Saha's credit that he unearthed this valuable document and used it as a plank to launch his own campaign.

8.8 Saha's campaign

Before "taming" a river, one must carry out a thorough study which must be in two parts: (i) Data collection, and (ii) controlled experiments in the laboratory or, simulation studies as we would refer to them today.

Data collection is an important prerequisite and in a willy-nilly way it goes on all the time. For example, there are the odd meteorological stations which record rainfall data but that is not enough. In the catchment area one needs a *network* of data collection centres (with today's technology, they can be made automatic). One must have information not only about the amount of rainfall but also the rate of precipitation (intensity of rain at a given time; this is very important when there is a downpour). Next, one must have detailed information about the topography of the terrain constituting the catchment area as well as the drainage area. (Here satellite photography can help.) Then one must have a pretty good idea of the nature of the soil, for this would determine how and where the river may change its course. Along the line, it is useful also to log the natural resources of the area — minerals, flora and fauna. This has become important particularly in view of ecological considerations as well as the exploitation of mineral wealth. Besides this, it is desirable to get as much information as possible about water flow paths in the past — this requires skillful detective work; the task is challenging, fascinating and useful.

Data collection is no doubt very necessary but not sufficient in itself. The data accumulated must be analysed, as Kepler did with Tycho's data. You might argue: "That was precise, astronomical data whereas here you are talking of multifarious pieces of information, some even qualitative." That might be so but it is precisely here that there is a greater need for a Sherlock Holmes.

Earlier I mentioned that Saha assisted Acharya Ray in 1922. Another of those whose services were requisitioned by the Acharya was P.C. Mahalanobis. The latter diligently analysed data collected earlier to reveal patterns which an ordinary mind could not perceive. Recognition of underlying patterns in the (wealth of) data accumulated is extremely important, and citing Mahalanobis' achievement Saha always stressed the need for intelligent post-processing of data; without that, the data was useless.

Data collection is fine and it provides an excellent base to start with. But one must do much more, and that is controlled experiments. Have you ever watched how water gathers and flows when there is a heavy downpour? In a city you would probably see nothing except water rushing down to choke drains and flood the streets, but if you are in open country, especially where the ground is sloping and barren, you would get a fascinating lesson in river physics. You will see tiny streams forming and linking, erosion, collapse of river banks, formation of gorges ... the whole works! A quick replay in half an hour or so of what happens over tens of thousands of years on a large scale. Why, I have seen many a time a miniature replica of the famed Grand Canyon! What this really tells us is that river behaviour can be studied using *scale models*. You could build a model of the terrain in the lab, allow water to sprinkle from above to mimic rain and see how it would flow. You could have sand, clay and other types of soils and see what happens. In this way, one would be able to predict with fair accuracy what would happen when there is a flooding due to heavy rainfall, what would happen when a bridge is constructed in a particular place, etc. Such knowledge would be extremely useful for, to be forewarned is to be forearmed.

Saha picked up where Sir Francis left off and conducted a sustained campaign for the establishment of a chain of full-fledged River Physics Laboratories. He wrote:

> The idea of a River Physics Laboratory is not new. England has no laboratory of this kind ... because England has no river problems on a scale as we have got in India ...

Europe, Russia and America were different. They all had big rivers, and to deal with their problems quite a few River Physics Laboratories had come into existence. Saha painstakingly reviewed the work done in these various places to highlight how useful and valuable controlled experiments had proved. India was a huge subcontinent with many rivers and the river systems were all *quite different* from each other. So there should be not one but a *chain* of labs, at least one for each region. Not only that; Saha spelt out in detail what the labs should do and added:

As the problems require expert knowledge of physics and mathematics, and demand much originality for their solutions, *the laboratory should have a research atmosphere*. It should be placed under a *distinguished physicist who is also well up in mathematics*. He should be provided with a good staff consisting of experts in allied lines, and a good laboratory. Such a laboratory should be attached to the Universities ...

8.9 Saha and the Damodar

Saha did not merely preach. He applied his mind keenly to the problem of repeated flooding by the Damodar River and (after conducting some modest experiments) evolved a detailed outline for harnessing its power. Let us start with Fig.8.4 which gives a rough overview of Damodar and its tributaries. The river along with its companions rises in the Chota Nagpur Hills and Saha says:

They run generally from north-west to south-east and empty their waters into the Hooghly River ... They have all the characteristics of hill rivers, that is, usually they run dry or have little water flowing in them, but when there is a large amount of precipitation in the hills, they become raging torrents, overflow the banks, burst through the embankments, and cause untold misery to the inhabitants.

Catastrophic floods occurred only once in a while and while they undoubtedly caused a lot of havoc, moderate floods which occurred more frequently were a different story. As a flood protection measure, embankments had been built in many places but peasants used to breach them to draw water for irrigation during normal times. When there was a moderate flood the waters would escape via the breaches and spread, but the effects were beneficial as they fertilised the soil and washed away the malarial larvae.

And then in 1850, the railways made their appearance and the authorities were "determined to tame the Damodar in order that the railway might be built." What did they do to subdue the river? They built many new embankments, closed the headwaters of the various breaches and "made breaches by men in the embankments which were needed for irrigating the fields, a criminal act." Result? Agricultural production declined, soil fertility decreased, unemployment rose, people started migrating to Calcutta and worst of all, a terrible malaria epidemic broke out. In one area, a *million* people died between 1850 and 1859. As Saha puts it, "Nature, vested interests and thoughtless management made a once prosperous valle· into a wilderness." What he now wanted was Nature, Man a Science to come together to make it again a "smiling garden."

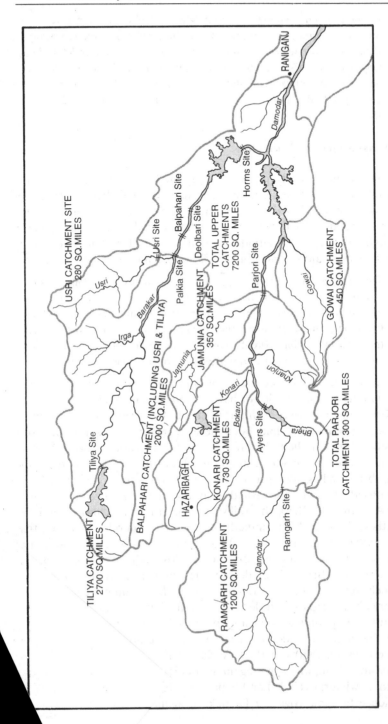

Fig.8.4 These two sketches taken from one of Saha's articles show (a) the rivers belonging to the Damodar family;

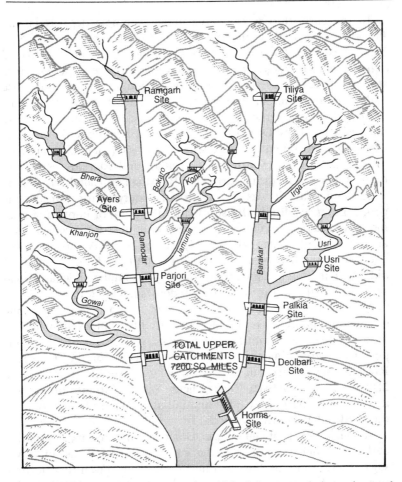

Fig.8.4 *continued* (b) the manner in which Saha wanted them dammed, tamed and harnessed.

Saha approached the problem like a true professional. In the thirties, a great river-harnessing scheme was executed in America which provided for Saha a wonderful model to copy. There is in the state of Tennessee in the United States, a river known as the Tennessee River. Before it was tamed, it was extremely erratic — let us just say it was rather like Damodar. Basically there were two problems — flooding and soil erosion. Everyone wanted something to be done but when it came to brasstacks there was nothing but conflict and disagreement amongst various vested interests and among the seven States (of the US) through which the river flowed. So nothing got done and this went on for decades.

In the early thirties came the great economic depression and President Roosevelt initiated a recovery plan known as the New Deal. Basically it consisted of a series of Government-managed activities which would provide employment and keep people from starving. America, as you know, is the citadel of private enterprise and capitalism, and state enterprise was anathema. But the public decided that state enterprise was preferable to starvation and did not resist the New Deal too much. Almost invariably the projects executed were intended to benefit society. (Incidentally one such project executed in South India over a hundred years ago when there was a severe drought was the Buckingham Canal. For nearly a hundred years it was a very useful waterway for transporting goods. Later it fell into disuse.) Under the guise of improving river navigation (a Federal Government responsibility), Roosevelt created an independent agency called the Tennessee Valley Authority (TVA) and gave it the task of doing all that people talked about but never did. And in a few short years the TVA completed what it was supposed to do and it was a tremendous success story.

Saha was greatly impressed, for here was a *concrete* example of a comprehensive, coordinated and scientific attack that he had all along been advocating. So impressed was he that he not only personally wrote many articles on the training of the Tennessee River (as he put it), but also got other professional friends to do likewise. The Tennessee River scheme was a glorious success and it was just crying to be copied and imitated. Where better to apply the model than on the Damodar?

Actually, the problem of the Damodar *had* received attention earlier. As Saha points out, the construction of dams, etc., was suggested as early as 1863 by one Lt. Garnault. From time to time surveys and studies were made, the last of them in 1919. Carried out by one Mr. E.L. Glass, they resulted in four volumes of reports (which, one suspects, were dutifully filed away!). Saha drew on all these, *and* the experience of the TVA.

It is not possible to review here Saha's master plan for the Damodar (published in 1944) but there is one passage I must quote as it is significant. In his model plan Saha says:

The Chota-Nagpur plateau from which the Damodar river and its tributaries emerge is mostly bare and denuded ... In the north ... there are extensive areas where all forests have entirely disappeared by repeated cutting, firing and uncontrolled grazing.

The bare areas are readily washed off and the rivers have to carry a heavy load of sand and silt. This deteriorates the channels of flow, and form sand bars and deltas near the mouth. The original soil gets more and more barren and has less power to soak and retain the rain waters.

It is highly desirable that the Government should take up the problem immediately and enforce laws for forest preservation ...

Please note this was a concern expressed almost half a century before all the current tear shedding about the environment.

8.10 The Damodar mess

So what happened to the Damodar River? Did anybody take Saha and his colleagues seriously and do anything about it? Apparently the Central Government did. It appointed in 1945 a Technical Advisory Committee under the chairmanship of one Mr. H.M. Mathews of the Central Technical Power Board. Interestingly, an important member of this Committee was Mr. W.L. Voorduin, who had earlier served on the TVA. He was specially recruited by the Government of India to advise it on the unified development of the Damodar River. The Committee produced a report and commenting on it Saha wrote (in 1946):

It is largely due to the series of articles published in *Science and Culture*, after the disastrous flood of the Damodar River in 1943, that public conscience was roused and the Central Government, under the guidance of the Hon'ble Dr. B.R. Ambedkar, took up the idea seriously ... It is surprising how closely the specific recommendations of the TVA expert agree with those given in this article [by Saha in 1944], though a sense of Government prestige has probably stood in the way of any acknowledgement being made. In fact, none has been made, but that does not matter. The people of Bihar and Bengal are vitally interested in the problem, and a good recommendation made with the prestige of a TVA expert is sure to evoke their good will and applause.

Saha reviewed critically and in detail the recommendations of the Mathews Committee and finally observed:

On the whole, we give our whole-hearted support to the general features of the scheme ... We hope the scheme will now be pushed through energetically and neither civil service, politicians, experts, or provincial jealousy will be allowed to impede its speedy execution.

Early 1947. India was in the throes of Independence and Jawaharlal Nehru assumed charge as the head of the Interim Government.

Politicians everywhere were anxious to please the public and made glib promises, including about power and river valley schemes. Saha was perturbed and expressing his concern he wrote:

> We welcome the revolutionary change in the outlook of the responsible members of the National Government and hail with delight Pandit Jawaharlal Nehru's speeches on Power Development, Dr. Rajendra Prasad's insistence on utilizing the latest scientific researches ... But while welcoming such measures, we shall be failing in our duty if we do not lay proper stress on the *magnitude of the task before us and the difficulties in giving concrete shape to them* ... A number of rivers have been earmarked for this [i.e., development] purpose. The case of Damodar was considered first ... The light hearted way in which these schemes are flashed in the radio and the press, gives rise to the impression that the plans of development may be achieved almost overnight, if only the country agrees to them. Such light-heartedness is fraught with grave consequences ...

Saha pleaded that one should not rush into action but must move forward only after detailed data collection and analysis, etc. Drawing upon the TVA experience, he specifically stressed the need for:

1. A thorough survey of the inherent character of the land and the natural resources — water, minerals, soil, vegetation.
2. Integrated planning with due attention to all aspects, i.e., power generation, navigation, irrigation, flood control, soil erosion, etc.

We skip the years and move on to 1954. Date, 6 April; occasion, a debate in the Lok Sabha on Multipurpose River Schemes. By this time, Saha was an Independent Member of Parliament (more about this in the last chapter). The Damodar Valley Project had meanwhile been started but, like most of our projects, promptly got into a mess.

It is interesting to read the transcript of the Lok Sabha Debate. There was Saha trying to pinpoint the causes for the mess and in the process, he wished to quote from a certain document. Immediately, a host of MP's were on their feet raising various technical objections — where did he (Saha) get the report from? They were more concerned about *how* Saha got the information than about the information itself. From the procedural point of view, technicalities are no doubt important but my experience has been that we almost always allow them to dominate, missing the main point.

I don't think we should spend any more time on the Damodar — it is anyway a sad story — but I must quote this bit from Saha's speech for it has a message. Saha was referring to how the

Damodar Valley Corporation (the analogue of the TVA) had a Chairman but no Chief Engineer. He said:

> The Corporation itself — or at least the late Chairman — was not very keen on taking a Chief Engineer because he [the Chairman, and obviously a civil "servant"] thought he could do the work of the Chief Engineer himself. After some time it was found that a civil servant might do anything, excepting converting a man into a woman ... Civil servants like liquid water cannot be fitted into any vessel and for specialist's work, *you must have a specialist* — you cannot leave it to a civil servant.

I shall have more to say about this later!

8.11 Why all this?

A long time has passed since the developments described in the preceding pages and you might well ask: "OK, Saha was interested in rivers and something he called river physics. But much has happened since then and dozens and dozens of new labs have been created. Surely this must include a few labs for hydraulic studies also. So what is there for physicists to worry about any more?" By way of answering that I would like to say that my purpose in describing Saha's interest in river physics was threefold. Firstly I wished to draw attention to Saha's wide range of interests, especially concerning matters that related to the technological and industrial advancement of the country. Secondly I wanted to lead on to the modern approach to simulation, which I shall do presently. Thirdly, this gives me an opening to discuss what might be called the social responsibility of physicists (and indeed scientists in general). I shall come to that after I have dealt with simulation.

8.12 Computer simulation

In olden times philosophers believed that Nature's mysteries could by unravelled by pure thought. However, this was not always possible and by the middle ages it became abundantly clear that theoretical studies had to be supplemented by experimental investigations; in fact, the two had to go hand in hand. Knowledge growth thus occurred according to the scenario in Fig.8.5.

The advent of the electronic computer has changed this picture and a new channel of investigation has been added namely, computer simulation. According to the dictionary, to simulate means to mimick. In the River Physics Laboratory that Saha clamoured for, he wanted scientists to build scale models of hilly terrains, river valleys, etc., and simulate floods, erosion, silting or whatever. Believe it or not, today much of all this can be done with a good

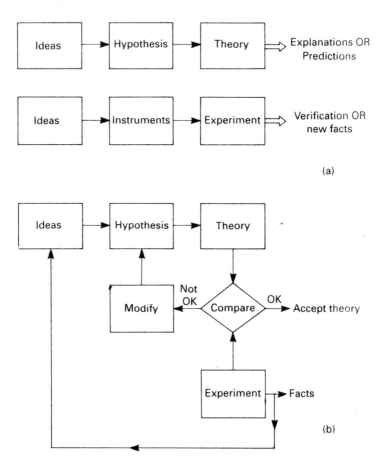

(a)

(b)

Fig.8.5 In science one tends to identify two distinct lines of approach namely, the theoretical and the experimental, as illustrated in (a). In ancient times, some philosophers believed that knowledge about Nature could be obtained by pure analytical reasoning. With the growth of science it has become quite clear that this is impossible. On the contrary, there is a delicate interplay between theory and experiment as shown in (b). At times theoretical predictions stimulate experiments (as happened in the case of general relativity) and at other times it is experiment which spurs theory (as frequently happens in high-energy physics). Theory and experiment are thus like the two strands of the DNA — both are needed!

computer. Such has been the incredible progress in computer technology that for something like Rs.20 lakhs, one can today get a computer with a capability exceeding that of a supercomputer of a decade ago, a computer which then cost around a million dollars or more. What does one do with such a computer? Well, one first inputs various mathematical models — of the terrain, of the nature of the soil, of the laws of erosion and so forth. Next one creates a particular situation, like: So much rain falls over such and such a region at such and such a rate. One now asks: "What happens?" Using the computer model one can literally follow instant by instant the situation as it develops. One can see erosion, river bursting the embankments, flooding and what not. Thanks to the power of computer graphics, one can also see on the computer screen all kinds of plots and even situation scenarios. After studying the results one might say: "OK, this shows that there could be trouble. Why don't I try to contain the trouble by doing the following?" In other words you have a possible solution. To find out how good it is, you now change your model to incorporate features representing the solution. Again you run through the *computer experiment* and look at the results. You might find that the solution attempted is in the

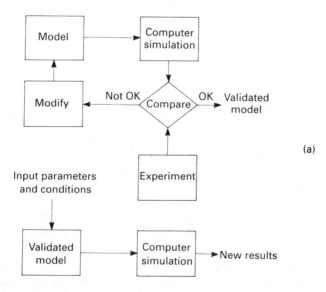

Fig.8.6 The advent of powerful computers has made it possible to simulate experiments (as discussed in the text). As a result, computer experiments have begun to play a role similar to that of lab experiments, vis-a-vis theory (see previous figure). However, computer experiments depend on the input model which has to be validated as shown in (a).

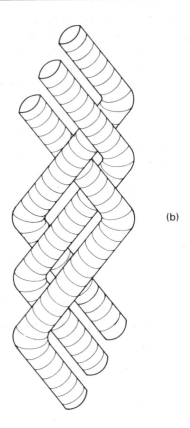

(b)

Fig.8.6 *continued* Simulations can then replace lab experiments *to the extent the model permits* — this limitation is important and must be clearly understood. Today it is no longer just theory and experiments; rather it is theory, experiments *and* computer simulation.' They are like the three strands of a triple helix (as one finds in collagen!). This is schematically brought out in (b).

right direction but needs tuning. So you change the model a bit more, and so on. I am sure you get the general idea — see also Fig.8.6. In short, the computer becomes the laboratory!

Computer simulation is big business today and is extensively used in all branches of basic research, from cosmology and seismology to molecular biology. In applied research and engineering, it is practically indispensible because it saves so much money. An oil-exploration company wants to build an off-shore platform. The platform must withstand corrosion, hurricane winds, tidal waves ... How to design it optimally? Computer simulation. The Hubble telescope launched into orbit a few years ago did not work properly. How to plan its repair using astronauts? Computer simulation again. Although computer simulation is extensively resorted to abroad, there is very little of it in the country.

Don't imagine that if you have a good computer all problems are solved! Far from it. Recall what Saha said about sound studies on rivers. Firstly he wanted good and extensive data. Next he wanted a "distinguished physicist who is also well up in mathematics." Those requirements remain. Without good baseline data one cannot construct a good input model; but mere data alone would not produce a good model — a good physicist is also required!

You might still ask: "Why a computer? Why not Saha's method of scale models?" Good question. Let me answer it by considering the case of aircraft design as it will convey the point better.

A modern aircraft is highly streamlined in shape. If it were not so, it would experience considerable air resistance while flying and that would increase fuel consumption. There are a number of other considerations as well but we shall not go into them — let us just stick to the shape question. What is the optimum shape for the aircraft of a certain size which is required to fly at a certain speed? In the old days they found this out by first constructing a scale model of the proposed aircraft. You might wonder how one can construct a model when one does not know the shape. There is a thing called experience you know, and drawing upon it one can have a *trial* shape. Next the model with this trial shape is placed in a wind tunnel. The latter is essentially a tunnel with a powerful fan at one end which can blow air. The fan is started, and some smoke is let in. The smoke is swept past the model and forms patterns which are then photographed and studied. If the trial shape is not good, then based on the results in the photographs one constructs an improved scale model, puts that in the wind tunnel and so on.

The wind tunnel experiments are no doubt straight forward (they are like the model river experiments that Saha advocated), but they are time consuming, especially when one has to try out many shapes and models. Making a good model of a fighter aircraft may take as much as six months. And when aircrafts have to fly at supersonic speeds and carry out manoeuvres, one does not take chances. *Many models have to be tested.* This enormously increases the time spent on design and that can make the cost astronomical. That is when aerodynamic engineers took to mimicking or simulating wind tunnel tests in the computer and presto, one "test" took only 3 hours. Further, changing the shape was no problem — it was just a question of tapping a few right keys! All at once, hundreds and hundreds of shapes could be explored in a few months and designers were deliriously happy. But the aircraft builders used to old wind tunnel tests were not too sure, and test pilots refused to risk flying a computer-designed aircraft! So a compromise was found. A proper wind tunnel test was carried out on the *best* shape recommended by the computer. If the results of the actual wind tunnel tests agreed with the computer simulation results, then the computer model was declared as valid, and the actual building of the aircraft was authorised.

Two things we learn from this. (i) Computer simulation can save time and (ii) simulation models must first be validated by comparison with real data before full faith is placed on them – see also Fig.8.6

8.13 A possible application for simulation

To get back to rivers, computers provide a powerful new means of studying and simulating river behaviour. I have no doubt that had Saha been alive today he would have vigourously championed computer simulation studies. Let me illustrate my point by considering the much-debated question about the dam across the Narmada River.

I am sure you have heard about the Narmada Valley problem. There are some people who want a dam across the river and there are others who don't. Both sides have arguments in support but they are so vehement in their respective beliefs that they simply will not give the other side a patient hearing. Narmada is a very complex problem and emotion is not the way to tackle it — it requires a *careful scientific study* and that precisely was the sort of thing Saha was constantly pleading for. Computer simulation backed by proper laboratory experiments could give a lot of insight into the Narmada problem, but that calls for extensive and high quality input data plus a competent team of modellers. One wonders if they are available.

Some people might say: "Look. The objection to the dam is related to a human problem and it has nothing to do with science." May be, but I suppose people are not stupid. If via detailed studies it can be established that the dam can bring maximum gain to the maximum number of people, then patiently the affected people can be won over, with due guarantee that they would not be left in the lurch.

Objections to dams are nothing new; they are age old. However, the question has to be tackled scientifically. If scientific studies show the dam is desirable then we go in for it; if it shows it is fraught with danger then we try to do something else. Anyway, I have not heard anybody even remotely suggesting a thorough computer simulation of the Narmada problem. After all, there is no Saha around to campaign for such indepth studies.

8.15 Physics and the applied sciences

I come now to what I regard as the underlying message behind Saha's interest in river physics. Saha was a first-rate scientist interested in profound problems like: "What goes on in stars?" His scientific training not only gave him a wide perspective but also equipped him to analyse problems in a scientific, logical and clearcut fashion. Indeed, good physicists are like that — that is one of the benefits of science; it inculcates a disciplined, rigorous and logical, i.e., scientific approach to problems.

Here we must pause and appreciate the special position of physics vis-a-vis the other natural sciences. Nobelist Rabi once succinctly observed: "Everything is to the left of physics". What he meant was essentially the following: To understand the *basic* process in any science or technology, one must ultimately turn to physics. Thus, whether it is the molecular structure of a drug, nerve conduction, ocean tides, plate tectonics — whatever; to understand the basics, we have no option but to go back to physics. The same is true of technology, especially the so-called high technology (hi-tech is the fashionable word for it). Whatever branch you take — fiber optics, satellite communication, lasers, sophisticated instrumentation technology — the fountainhead is again physics. If there is any science that stands somewhat aloof from the parade of natural sciences, it is mathematics, but we shan't go into that here.

So there it is, the pecking order; whether one likes it or not, physics *is* the Gangotri if I may say so. Today there is a fair amount of research in basic physics going on in India. Is it making any visible and coherent impact on, say, our industry? Sad to say, hardly any. In America, Russia, Europe and Japan, it is a different story. Physics there spreads out like a delta enriching allied areas and in the process deriving nourishment itself — see Fig. 8.7. In America, for example, the physics community is not only highly regarded but also carries a clout. Its views are heard with respect by the Government, Congress *and* the Industry. In fact in the post-Second World War era, American Industry has been a mighty beneficiary of physics research.

Some years ago, President Reagan initiated a mind-boggling defence project called Star Wars. The expenditure involved was so

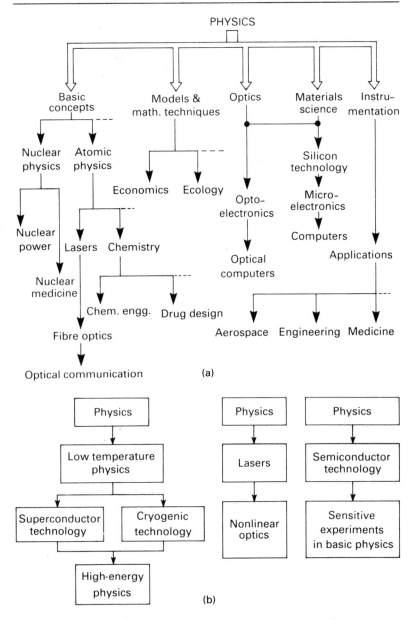

Fig.8.7 To describe the influence and the impact of physics on other branches of science and on engineering would require a whole volume. Part (a) captures a tiny fragment of this diversified impact. Part (b) indicates how physics first spurs technology and then derives benefit to improve itself. The process of rejuvenation repeats cyclically!

huge that many strongly objected to it. The American Physical Society (APS) commissioned a scientific study on the Star Wars Project. It was carried out by N. Bloembergen (Nobel Prize winner) and C.K.N. Patel (inventor of the famous CO_2 laser). They came to the conclusion that from a purely scientific point of view, the Star Wars System would simply not work. This was a big blow to the President and eventually the project was quietly buried.

In India, the physics community is a nonentity. A few physicists are individually well known but the professional bodies are ignored by everyone including the Government. For this, our physicists themselves are to blame. Most of them prefer to remain in "ivory towers". In a sense this is good but too much of it can be counter-productive.

A few years ago I was the President of the Indian Physics Association (IPA). During my term, the Raman Centenary occurred and the IPA wanted to bring out a special issue of its journal *The Physics News* to commemorate the event. But our kitty was empty and I had to run with a begging bowl from pillar to post to scrape together the paltry sum of twenty thousand rupees needed for the purpose. Compared to that, our professional engineering bodies are quite well off — they have good corpus funds and even buildings of their own.

Many a time I have discussed this with my physicist friends. Their argument is: "Our community is rather small and we can't fritter away our energies in societal activities. Anyway, all the cross-fertilisation you want is taking place abroad and we just have to import." What if import is blocked? You think it does not happen? Find out about India's efforts to import liquid hydrogen rocket engines for our space programme.

Let us for the moment agree that the Indian physics community is miniscule and that it cannot make an impact on our Industry. At least it can do something to improve the teaching of physics in India and also physics teachers in our schools and colleges. Is it doing anything significant in that respect? I wonder.

The sad part of it all is that we have today a sizable number of very competent research physicists. But, for reasons of their own, they have adopted a Brahminical attitude — stay aloof. Maybe it assures career progress and survival. Does it really, if research has to survive largely on foreign contacts, imported instruments, imported samples, etc.? Our Industry gets precious little from our scientists engaged in basic research and so it has resorted to import left and right. True there are all kinds of problems in bringing about a dialogue between our physics community and our Industry. But who will solve them if we all choose to turn the other way? This is where one must really admire Saha. He was second to none in his love for pure science. But he also loved this country and had a deep feeling for its people. He passionately wanted our people also to get the benefits of modern science and technology, just as people in the advanced countries are getting. His preoccupation with rivers was but just *one* aspect of his intense social commitment.

Dear young reader! You don't have to copy my generation. Instead, copy Saha. He was a much better role model. After all, this is your country too. Maybe we forgot. I hope at least you won't.

9 *The Final Innings*

9.1 Introduction

When scientists grow older, they usually switch from active involvement in basic research to other activities like teaching, science management, etc. Very few, like Raman, remain wedded to research all their lives. There is nothing wrong in changing tracks and in fact we owe much to elders who have moved over to other areas, carrying with them valuable knowledge and experience. When Saha returned to Calcutta in 1938, he officially donned the mantle of the Palit Professor of Physics in the Calcutta University but the role he actually played was very much larger.

9.2 Institute of Nuclear Physics

Till 1934, the Palit Chair was held by Raman who mainly conducted his research at the Indian Association for the Cultivation of Sciences (IACS). When Raman left, one or two of his students were pursuing studies on the Raman effect in the University with the modest facilities available there. D.M. Bose who stepped in following the departure of Raman allowed the continuation of this work, and did not bring about any major change in the University Physics Department. However, things were different when Saha entered the picture. Recognising that nuclear physics was rapidly gaining in importance, he straightaway revised the curricula to provide a prominent place for this new and exciting subject. In fact, Saha was the first to introduce nuclear physics into the country in a University or elsewhere. Bhabha came later, but then his interests lay beyond nuclear physics, i.e., in particle physics (see *Bhabha and His Magnificent Obsessions*).

As mentioned earlier, Saha's interest in nuclear physics was aroused during his foreign trip in 1936–37. Impressed particularly with what he saw in Berkeley (see section 6.6), he sent in 1938 his student B.D. Nag Chowdhary to Berkeley to study and work under Lawrence, and learn all he could about the cyclotron. Saha was keen to have a cyclotron in the Calcutta University and used his influence with Nehru to persuade the Tatas to give him a grant to build one. The Tatas obliged with Rs.60,000/- which was no doubt a lot of money in those days, but far from sufficient for building a cyclotron. As in Allahabad, hunting for money now became an important occupation. In 1941 Nag Chowdhary returned, and thanks to his efforts in America a consignment of cyclotron parts (mainly for making the magnet) soon followed. Meanwhile America entered the war and the ship carrying the next batch of equipment (mainly vacuum pumps) was sunk by the Japanese. This was a major setback and now there was no hope of getting any parts from America; anyway, American scientists, Lawrence included, had drifted to war work. The parts now all had to be made in Calcutta, and this proved an interminable affair. Eventually it took many, many years for the cyclotron to be completed (if I am not mistaken, it finally worked after Saha passed away). Apart from this, Saha also started on a modest scale some cosmic-ray observations in Darjeeling.

After the war the world heard about the atomic bomb and all of a sudden the public realised (at least vaguely) the profound importance of atomic energy (or nuclear energy as it is more appropriately called). Training in nuclear physics now assumed a new importance and Saha felt that he should expand his activities in the University by establishing an autonomous Institute under the umbrella of the University. This was no easy task as he had to battle for funds on the one hand and against red tape on the other. Finally in 1948 he was able to have the foundation stone laid by Dr. Shyama Prasad Mookerjee, son of Sir Ashutosh Mookerjee. The building was declared open in 1951 by Madame Joliot Curie, whose husband not only won the Nobel Prize (for his work on radioactivity) but also did pioneering work on nuclear chain reaction during the early days of the war. We shall briefly come back to the story of this Institute of Nuclear Physics in a later section.

9.3 Saha and the IACS

As per the University regulations, Saha had to retire in 1952 both from the Palit Professorship and the post of the Director of the Institute of Nuclear Physics. However he retained his links with the Institute in an honorary capacity.

Retirement did not mean cessation of work. On the contrary, Saha remained busy as ever. Right from the early thirties Saha was deeply interested in the IACS. In fact, there then was once a clash of ideas between him and Raman (who was the Honorary

President of the IACS at that time). After his return to Calcutta in 1938, Saha again began to devote time to the Association. In 1944 he became the Honorary Secretary, and following the death of the then President in 1946, himself became the President. At that time the IACS was located at 210 Bow Bazaar Street (which is where Raman made his famous discovery). Following that glorious era, the Association sort of plodded on and Saha was keen now to inject fresh life by starting several new research programmes. All this called for careful planning and took enormous time and effort. Realising that the Bow Bazaar premises were no longer adequate Saha looked for an alternate, more spacious site. But land costs money, and once again the search was on for cash. Eventually he was able to persuade the Government of West Bengal to part with some money and ten acres of land were purchased in Jadhavpur. New buildings were built and the Bow Bazaar lab faded into history.

Obeying the Association rules, Saha stepped down as President in 1950. Meanwhile, Bhatnagar (recall the reference to him in an earlier chapter) who had risen high in Delhi and established many a national laboratory suggested that it was time that the IACS had a full-time Director. He further insisted that the post be offered to Saha so that he could complete the reorganisation work he had started earlier. Thus in 1953, Saha became the first Director of IACS, a post he held till his death in 1956.

9.4 Saha and atomic energy

We saw earlier that Saha attended an International Conference on Nuclear Physics in Bohr's institute in 1937. On his return to India he used his favourite organ *Science and Culture* (see section 9.5) to give a detailed report on what happened during the conference. As further evidence of his growing interest in matters nuclear, he published in 1940 a long paper on what we would today describe as nuclear systematics.

Saha was aware of the electrifying discovery of nuclear fission by Hahn and Meitner in 1939, and the stupefying possibilities it held. In March 1941 he gave a lecture on fission to the Indian Physical Society. Thanks to the gathering war clouds, very little on fission physics was published soon after the discovery of the basic phenomenon; one may say it went underground! Nevertheless, Saha was able to surmise many things. For instance he said:

> By fissioning completely one gram of uranium, we obtain as much energy as is obtained by burning about 2 tons of coal.

It might be argued that this does not say anything more than that $E = mc^2$. In that case, consider the following observation made in the same lecture:

> It is also possible that a process may be discovered which would render the reactions to proceed with explosive violence ... A tablet of U^{235}, no more than a homeopathic globule in size, may blow off a mighty Super Dreadnought [a great big battleship of those days] — a feat which can at the present time be performed only by a torpedo carrying several tons of explosives ...

This was in March 1941, more than a year before Fermi first achieved a controlled, self-sustaining fission reaction and roughly four and half years before the first atomic bomb was test fired (in the deserts of New Mexico in America).

In the years that followed, Saha was probably often thinking about atomic energy but there was very little news available; we now know why.

Meanwhile, in 1940 the British rulers in Delhi formed a Board for Scientific and Industrial Research (BSIR) with Dr. S.S. Bhatnagar as the Head. Saha was invited to be a Member. The Government, following the example of England, wanted the BSIR to advise it on how Indian Industry could contribute to the war effort (perhaps you remember that the Second World War broke out in 1939). In 1942, the Government constituted a superior body called the Council of Scientific and Industrial Research (CSIR). Originally the Government wanted only industrialists and administrators on the Governing Council. When this became known, Bhatnagar and all the other scientist members of the BSIR threatened that they would resign. The Government then backed off and included a few scientists in the Governing Council, and Saha was one of them.

By 1944 it became clear that the tide of fortune in the war was turning against Germany and Japan. In anticipation of victory, the British Government began to make plans for post-war reconstruction. As a part of this process, it asked the Royal Society to send Prof. A.V. Hill to India to advise the British India Government. Hill came and met many scientists, Saha included. He then recommended that an Indian Scientific Mission (ISM) be sent abroad to observe scientific and industrial progress and make post-war plans. Hill's recommendation was accepted and a delegation left India in October 1944; Saha was a member of the ISM.

The tour took the Mission to several countries including America. While there, Saha made many enquiries about research on atomic energy but drew a blank. He did not know that right then, atomic energy research was the most closely guarded secret. Realising that Saha could get into trouble with his inquisitive questions, an American friend hinted that Saha would be better off if he desisted from asking questions. Meanwhile, the Federal Bureau of Investigation (FBI) somehow got wind of the fact that Saha was asking too many questions and arranged for sleuths to keep a watch. On the day prior to departure, Saha was interrogated by FBI experts. They were astounded that he knew a lot about the basics of atomic energy but were relieved that he knew nothing of what was actually going on in the US right then.

On return to India the ISM prepared an official report and submitted it to the Government; the report was drafted by Saha. But Saha also wrote to Nehru who by now had been released from prison. (Along with Gandhi, Nehru and several others were put in prison in 1942 following the Quit-India movement.) In his letter Saha said, "... I am very anxious to meet you and relate to you all my experiences in the UK, USA and Soviet Union." Why Saha specially wrote to Nehru would become clearer shortly.

In 1947 India became free but in the process the country was literally torn apart. However, there was also much expectation, especially with Nehru having become the Prime Minister. Atomic energy was the new hope and as a Member of the BSIR, Saha had every reason to believe that he would be able to play a key role in the development of atomic energy in India. Bhabha also had similar thoughts and he too began to offer ideas to Nehru on this subject (see *Bhabha and His Magnificent Obsessions*). In 1948, Saha was formally asked by the Government (at Nehru's instance of course) about the formation of an Atomic Energy Commission (AEC) which Bhabha had suggested. Saha firmly opposed it on the ground that (i) India lacked the industrial base and (ii) trained manpower was not available. In Saha's view, before launching a full-fledged atomic energy programme with an AEC and all that, the industry ought to be built up first. In addition, nuclear physics- and nuclear energy-oriented courses ought to be introduced in the various universities to train the necessary manpower. To him, Bhabha's plan seemed like putting the cart before the horse. Saha strongly advocated the French model of atomic energy development which was the brainchild of his friend Joliot Curie. (Like Saha, Joliot Curie also had very strong leftist feelings.) Bhabha, on the other hand, advocated a faster and more vigorous programme of development which appealed to Nehru. Thus Saha quickly lost the advantage of all his earlier association with Nehru, and Bhabha walked away with the cake! This must have been a bitter disappointment to Saha, a feeling reflected in many a critical remark he later made on atomic energy development. In 1954 Saha complained:

> India has got an AEC and five years ago we had announced that we were going to set up a nuclear reactor within five years. This is 1954 and the reactor has not been set up.

Actually, it was not all that bad. India's first reactor Apsara was commissioned in 1956 (see the companion volume on Bhabha), a wee bit late may be but not very late, especially considering how much projects get delayed these days.

It is no secret that Saha disagreed with the way Bhabha was going about the atomic energy programme. His feeling was that Bhabha's approach would not deliver the goods. Writing in 1954 he felt that India, like France, must aim at nuclear autonomy, i.e., should not be dependent on foreign powers. He said:

> For this purpose, a Central Atomic Energy Laboratory is needed whose aim should be:
> (a) To organise prospecting work for uranium and thorium ...
> (b) To process ore to metal ...
> (c) To build reactors out of Indian material ...
> (d) To organise a Central Service for Atomic Energy work in the country.

A year later he attended a conference on atomic energy in Moscow and on return seemed depressed about the way the Indian programme was shaping. Echoing his feelings he lamented:

> What concerns us deeply is: When can we hope to have our own atomic energy industry in India like the more fortunate nations ...

Unfortunately, Saha died soon after he wrote this, but much of what he wanted and dreamt of were *actually achieved and reasonably quickly too*, as you will find if you read the companion volume on Homi Bhabha.

The Saha–Bhabha differences are a matter of history and in recalling them, I am not making any value judgement. Writing shortly after Saha's death, D.M. Bose put Saha's attitude in the proper perspective. Bose said:

> The role of Saha was that of an evangelist who preached a new gospel, and later on that of an uncompromising critic, when he believed that his programme [or whatever it was, especially planning, as you will read in a later section] after being accepted, was being mismanaged during implementation. Like all evangelists, Saha took a simplified picture of the nature of the problems... The problems of

human factor, its limitations due to existing social and economic conditions prevailing in the country, the respective role of persuasion versus compulsion [i.e., democracy versus dictatorship], were not explicitly taken into consideration by him. This is in the nature of things; an evangelist can only have a simplified vision of the problems he envisages and the solution he offers.

There is no doubt, as Bose says, that Saha was driven by a moral passion for the achievement of social justice. But he could seldom agree with the way things were done and till the end he often found himself in the opposition.

To wrap up the story on atomic energy, in 1954 Saha had a meeting with Bhabha (who was now firmly in the saddle as far as atomic energy was concerned), and an arrangement was worked out whereby the Institute of Nuclear Physics would receive Rs.50 lakhs for the duration of the Second Five Year Plan. Compared to the meagre funding earlier received, this was a great windfall. What is more pleasing is that personal differences if any between the two giants did not come in the way of a larger cause. Indeed, over the years the Institute now appropriately renamed as the Saha Institute of Nuclear Physics (SINP) has not only been receiving a very much higher funding (practically all from the Department of Atomic Energy) but also has a modern building in a new campus right next to a cyclotron laboratory (VECC) set up by the Bhabha Atomic Research Centre, Bombay. I had the pleasure and the privilege of serving on the Council of the SINP during the eighties, and during my period a strong beginning was made in a new area, i.e., plasma physics. In many respects SINP is now like TIFR, and well known nationally as well as internationally. That surely would have pleased Saha very much. On the whole one might say that both the atomic energy programme and his cherished institute have grown precisely the way Saha dreamt of.

9.5 Saha in public life

We come now to the most important aspect of Saha's life, namely his involvement in public affairs. Saha was always public spirited, as is evident from his participation during his school days in a boycott against the British Governor (see Chapter 1). In college his spirit was further kindled by Acharya P.C. Ray, an ardent nationalist in addition to being a great teacher and an eminent chemist. Thus when the Acharya organised flood relief, Subhas Bose and Saha readily volunteered help (as has been described in an earlier chapter). Saha also participated in a Youth Conference organised by Bose in 1921. Speaking then, Saha said:

> The lethargy and the dependence on others which have become a part of our national character must be replaced by self-reliance and hard work.

Seventy and odd years later, we are still to do that!

9.5.1 Getting out of the ivory tower

We have already seen that despite his patriotic disposition, Saha refrained from participating in the freedom struggle. Family responsibilities compelled him to take a job, and the job he got led him to the exciting pastures of science. Becoming absorbed in research he then entered what is usually described as the *ivory tower*. Most scientists remain all their lives in the ivory tower bothering little about anything other than their work, including their own home and society. In the advanced countries (where the basic problems of poverty, health and illiteracy have all been banished), this luxury of retreat into the ivory tower is excusable, but in a country like India it is not. Saha's withdrawal was only temporary and slowly he drifted out. As he once put it:

> Scientists are often accused of living in the *ivory tower* and not troubling their mind with realities and apart from my association with political movements in my juvenile years, I had lived in the ivory tower upto 1930. But science and technology are very important for administration nowadays at least as much as law and order. I have gradually glided into politics because I wanted to be of some use to the country in my own humble way.

At first Saha confined himself mainly to organisational matters relating to science. Thus it was that he became involved in the early thirties with the affairs of the IACS (leading to a controversy with Raman). Later he founded two academies, as described in an earlier chapter. Meanwhile in 1934 he founded the journal *Science and Culture* and shortly afterwards, the Indian Science News Association (ISNA). Thereafter, *Science and Culture* became the official organ of ISNA. When he finally returned to Calcutta, his office in the Science College was next door to the office of ISNA. As Saha's student Santimay Chatterjee puts it,

> Saha at last found a medium to express his ideas and a flood gate was opened. In the first year [of publication of *Science and Culture*], he

himself contributed thirteen entries. His total contribution to the journal over the years number one hundred and thirty six, the last one being published after his demise.

Saha never wrote casually. Every piece of writing was preceded by intense study and careful researching, and no wonder the great libraries of Calcutta (and later the Parliament Library in Delhi) became his favourite haunts.

There was no aspect of national life that escaped Saha's attention and comments; he touched upon everything, including the constitution. Unlike journalists and editors who merely write and pontificate, Saha also became involved and tried to contribute wherever possible. Thus he not only preached calendar reform but served on committees set up for that purpose. He not only advocated river management but actually carried out modest simulation studies on the Damodar and evolved a blue print; and so on.

9.5.2 Involvement with planning

On the national front, his involvement with planning was perhaps the most intense. It is also an absorbing story which reveals much about the man. As a keen student of history, Saha was no doubt fascinated by the rise and fall of various civilizations and empires, but at the same time he was also following with keen interest the remarkable transformation taking place in Russia after the revolution in October, 1917. By inclination Saha was a leftist and it was no wonder he was attracted to the Soviet model of development (as Nehru also was).

The first occasion to become involved with the planning process at least in a modest way arose out of the seminar on power he organised while in Allahabad (see Chapter 6). You will recall that Nehru called for concrete proposals and under Saha's leadership the National Academy of Sciences duly responded.

At this stage we must take a peep into the politics of the country as it then prevailed. Following the modest political reform initiated by the British in 1935, something like popular elections were held in 1937. The result was that in most of the Provinces, the Congress was swept to power. In U.P. Nehru became the Premier (as the Chief Minister was then called) and one member of his cabinet was Dr. Kailas Nath Katju, an eminent lawyer (and also an ardent fan of Sherlock Holmes). According to Saha, Katju hastened his exit from the ivory tower. Let us hear Saha tell the story.

Dr. Katju was invited in 1938 to open a match factory somewhere in the United Provinces, where he delivered a very eloquent speech saying that a great leap was taken towards large-scale industrialisation! This speech gave me a rude shock, for it disclosed that a top-ranking congress leader, entrusted with the important task of re-organising, improving, and initiating industries of his province has revealed by his speech that he has no idea of what large-scale industrialisation was. I found this to be the case with most elderly congressmen who were defacto or potential ministers, and could foresee that when in power, they would be like landsmen who have never seen large sheets of water and still asked to pilot ships in the ocean. It was these considerations which led me to apply my mind to the problem.

Again some background is necessary. As you must be aware, although there were many leaders during the freedom struggle, towering above them all was Mahatma Gandhi. Gandhiji was firmly wedded to the principle of plain living and high thinking and he made no secret that this was also his dream for the Nation. In other words, he was not exactly enamoured of huge industries that Nehru seemed so fond of. Many in the Congress subscribed to Gandhiji's views because to them it implied a restoration of ancient and traditional values. The symbol of all this was the *charka* or the spinning wheel, and I am sure you have seen pictures of Gandhi spinning away. Congress volunteers in hundreds and thousands took eagerly to the charka, spun yarn and took pride in wearing dress made out of cloth woven from such yarn, i.e., *khadi* or *khaddar* as it then used to be called. According to Gandhi, khaddar would promote self-employment and free us from dependence on the mills of Lancashire (in England; cloth in the twenties and thirties used to be largely imported from England).

Saha was vehemently opposed to all this. To him, khaddar and charka were symbols of medieval times and he often sarcastically referred to such attitudes as bullock-cart philosophy or back-to-the-Vedas outlook. His revered teacher P.C. Ray gave up Western dress, took to khaddar and also strongly advocated it, which upset Saha very much. At that time he was working in Allahabad and whenever he came to Calcutta he called on Acharya Ray. Inevitably the talk would turn to Gandhian philosophy and Saha would return shaking his head. Once Ray asked Saha why he avoided khaddar. Saha tersely replied, "khaddar is often used to hide a multitude of sins and as I have no sins to hide, I do not feel the need to wear khaddar." But it must be said that this ideological difference never came in the way of cordial relations between the student and his teacher, and Saha always remained reverential to Ray.

After this preamble, let us get back to Katju's speech. To Saha it was like red rag to a bull. At long last the country was on the doorstep of independence, and instead of making serious plans for massive industrialisation, here was a senior leader and an industries minister to boot treating the subject almost flippantly. It all smacked of the famous bullock-cart philosophy and warning bells began to ring for Saha.

Meanwhile, Netaji Subhas Chandra Bose was elected the President of the Indian National Congress in 1938, and to Saha this was a shot in the arm. On August 21, 1938, the Indian Science News Association invited Bose to a function during which Saha pointedly asked Bose:

> May I enquire whether the India of the future is going to revive the philosophy of village life, of bullock-cart, thereby perpetuating servitude or is she going to be a modern industrialised nation ...
>
> I put the question because the Congress has come to power in several provinces and because there is a great confusion of ideas regarding the future industrialisation of India.

In his reply Bose said:

> We want, first and foremost, the aid of science in this task [industrialisation] ...
>
> India is still in the pre-industrial stage of evolution. No industrial advancement is possible until we first pass through the throes of an industrial revolution. Whether we like it or not, we have to reconcile ourselves to the fact that the present epoch is the industrial epoch in modern history. There is no escape from the industrial revolution. We can at best determine whether this revolution, that is industrial, will be a comparatively gradual one, as in Great Britain, or a forced march as in Soviet Russia. *I am afraid that it has to be a forced march in this country.*

This was naturally music to Saha's ears. It now remained to ensure that Bose could translate words into action. Saha therefore advised Bose that in his capacity as the Congress President, he should call a conference of the industries ministers of Congress-ruled Provinces and form a National Planning Committee (NPC). Bose readily agreed and the meeting was set for October 1938; Saha was asked to attend as an invitee.

Came October, and Saha went to Delhi to attend the meeting convened by Bose. Unfortunately he arrived one day late and to his dismay found that the NPC had already been formed and that the venerable Sir M. Visvesvaraya was being requested to Chair the Committee. Now Visvesvaraya was a highly respected son of India with a creditable record of public service, wide experience in engineering, etc., (see Box 9.1). On the face of it therefore, he was an excellent choice. However, Saha saw it otherwise. He felt that Visvesvaraya might be soft to the Gandhians and not press hard for a crash and heavy industrialisation programme. Someone tougher and with a Marxist leaning was needed, and in Saha's mind that someone was none other than Nehru himself. But right then Nehru was in Europe attending on his ailing wife (who eventually died in a Swiss sanatorium). Perhaps it was his physical absence that made people think of other names for the NPC Chairmanship.

Box 9.1 You may be wondering who this Sir M. Visvesvaraya is. The best way of satisfying your curiosity is to reproduce (in part) what appeared in *Science and Culture* in December 1941. Probably, the article was written by Saha himself.

Sir Mokshagundam Visvesvaraya, now in his 81st year, was born of humble parents in the village of Chickballapur (Mysore State) on September 15, 1861. They were blessed with this child after a pilgrimage to Benares and their offerings at the sacred temple of Lord Visvesvara on the banks of the Ganges. Hence the name Visvesvaraya. He was educated at the Central College, Bangalore where he took his B.A. degree in 1881. He had his engineering education at the College of Science, Poona [now Pune], where he topped the list thus securing for himself the guaranteed post of assistant engineer in the Bombay Public Works Department in 1884. While in Bombay service, he was associated with the design, construction and administration of a large number of irrigation and water-supply schemes. He retired at his own request in 1908. On this occasion Sir John Muir Mackenzie, senior member of the Bombay Executive Council said:

... The development of this system [Block system] is due entirely to the genius of Mr. Visvesvaraya, certainly one of the ablest officers, European or Indian, of the Public Works Department, with whom it has been my pleasure and honour to work.

In 1904 he was appointed special consulting Engineer to the Government of His Exalted Highness the Nizam of Hyderabad when he was placed in charge of flood protection in the Musi River and underground sewage works in Hyderabad city. Between 1909 and 1912 he was Chief Engineer and Secretary to the Government of Mysore in the Public Works and Railway Departments. During this period, the dam across Cauvery, forming the reservoir known as Krishnarajasagara, the then largest reservoir in India was constructed. This gave an impetus to hydro-electric power development and has thus enabled Mysore to launch bold industrial schemes ... He was appointed Dewan of Mysore in 1912 and he continued in that office till 1919. During this period he was mainly responsible for bringing into existence a university for Mysore, an Iron and Steel Works at Bhadravati, a Sandal Oil Factory, the Bank of Mysore, the Soap Factory, the Engineering College, a Village Improvement Scheme and a system of economic investigation and planning for district ...

After relinquishing office, he toured around the world for over a year. His administrative and political knowledge have since then been utilized by one government after another in British India and Indian States ...

Honours come thick on him — C.I.E. in 1911, K.C.I.E. in 1915, honorary degrees of doctorate of Calcutta (1923), Bombay (1931), and Benares (1937).

Sir Visvesvaraya lives a simple, almost ascetic life. Whether in office or retirement, his daily routine is methodical, and he follows the maxim which he once placed before a students' gathering at his old school — 8 hours for work, 8 hours for sleep and 8 hours for food, exercise, recreation etc. ...

We have every hope that Sir M. Visvesvaraya will easily score his century.

He did!

Saha immediately sought Sir M. Visvesvaraya, had a long chat with him and managed to dissuade him from accepting the Chairmanship. Later he recalled:

I told him [Visvesvaraya] that unless a top-ranking Congressman was made the Chairman [Visvesvaraya did not belong to the Congress], the decisions of the National Planning Committee would be regarded as merely academic and would have no value in the eyes of the Congress. The grand old man saw the force of the argument, and readily agreed. It was at my suggestion that Pt. Jawaharlal Nehru, then in Europe, was invited to take up the Chairmanship of the proposed Committee.

Eventually, the NPC functioned from Bombay with Nehru as the Chairman. Several expert sub-Committees assisted the NPC, and one of these was headed by Saha. The final report required 27 volumes! But it was not smooth sailing as we shall presently see.

In the midst of all the above, there was trouble within the Congress.In 1939 Bose sought re-election as President and won despite opposition from Gandhiji. But shortly afterwards he resigned realising that without Gandhi's support he could not function effectively. In between, Saha was getting nervous whether Nehru himself was becoming soft and yielding to the Gandhians while evolving the National Plan. He aired his misgivings orally and in letters to friends, and word of this reached Nehru. Piqued, Nehru wrote in a letter to Acharya Kripalani:

> He [Saha] has referred to me repeatedly and made various statements regarding me which are bound to convey an entirely wrong impression of what I said in the Planning Committee ... [The charges about Congress leaders being puppets in the hands of industrialists] are really extraordinary, and shows Professor Saha is not conversant with what has been happening in India. [It is] amazing, and displays a lack of appreciation of the whole political, social and economic events in the recent history of India. It is unfortunate that Professor Saha's letter has been written in a spirit which is far from scientific or dispassionate.

So there it was, the first sign of discord. Eventually, the gap widened, as we shall soon see.

In September 1939 the Second World War broke out, promptly throwing everything out of gear. As a colony of Britain, India was automatically dragged into the war. The Congress objected and all the popular governments resigned. Politically it was now back to square one, with the added rigidity of a war-time environment. In 1942 Gandhi gave the call to the British to Quit India and the British responded by promptly throwing all the leaders, Nehru included, into prison. Bose was placed under house arrest but he escaped, went to Japan, formed the Indian National Army and fought a military battle against the British on the Eastern sector. Sometime towards the end of the war he died, presumably in a plane crash. I am sure you know the rest of the story.

9.5.3 Widening gap with Nehru

Came Independence, and Nehru assumed the Prime Ministership. As far as Saha was concerned, the ball was now in Nehru's court. In his book *Discovery of India* which Nehru wrote in prison, he had reflected deeply on the model of industrial development which India should pursue, and they were in tune with Saha's ideas. Now that he was in the saddle, was Nehru going to stand by what he wrote? Saha waited and watched. As he did so, it seemed to Saha that Nehru was dragging his feet. It also became clear that despite their earlier cordial association, Nehru was no longer close. And where atomic energy was concerned there was an obvious preference for Bhabha. The rift was now wide and Saha could read the writing on the wall; but there was nothing much he could do.

Though shut out in certain sectors (e.g., atomic energy) it did not mean that Saha was totally kept out. For example, he was nominated a Member of the University Education Commission of which Dr. S. Radhakrishnan was the Chairman. (Later Radhakrishnan became the Vice President, and still later the President of India.)

Saha always had a deep interest in education, and I mean not merely physics education. He has explained his reasons:

> It has been the great lesson of history that a democracy cannot properly function unless the voters are nearly hundred percent literate. Nearly hundred years ago [Saha wrote this in 1952], when democracy was first coming to England, John Stuart Mill made the prophetic remark that *"Universal suffrage without universal education will be a curse."* ...
>
> Take for example the USA. Until education had been made compulsory, elections were managed by party bosses and democracy was a mockery.

How true all this is even today, nearly half a century after Independence! Education, primary education especially, has been callously neglected and illiteracy has been indirectly encouraged as it facilitates easy manipulation of voters. And in recent times, we seem to have discovered that the best way to march forward is by going backward — I am referring to the clamour of every community to be labelled backward. Saha worried about going back to the Vedas — at least in Vedic times there was knowledge and wisdom; now we seem set for the stone age.

All this talk of reservation which we hear so often is nothing new. It existed in an embryonic form much earlier, and commenting on it Saha wrote in 1945:

> India is now passing through a very critical stage of her political history. The different political parties in India are at present torn off by conflicting ideologies and there is no unity of purpose. Feelings of individualism based on sectarian, religious and provincial prejudices have been far more predominant than of rationalism ...

Turning then to quota in jobs for the various communities, Saha says:

> To some extremists, freedom lies in gaining some percentage in the services. Under this confusion, the central fact of the co-ordinated development of natural resources on strictly nationalistic lines is completely lost sight of. What else but poverty and misery can the poor heirs of a poor man get after division? The extreme poverty of the country is a glaring reminder that a mere increase in the allotment of services by 1 or 2 percent, cannot solve the eternal problem of the masses of India. A poor man will remain poor whether he gets 30 percent or 33 percent.

Saha always pleaded for widening the educational base but that was never done. Instead, the educational sector was squeezed and now the easy way out seems to be reservation; and why not, if it will fetch votes?

9.5.4 Saha and bureaucrats

From the British we inherited an administration that was trained in the maintenance of law and order and in revenue collection. After Independence, the scenario completely changed and all of a sudden the country embarked on major ventures. However, the administrative culture remained stagnant, causing severe problems. Elsewhere I have described how Bhabha complained about it; now let us hear Saha:

> An unfortunate aspect is the reservation of several important posts for the Indian Civil Service [then it was the ICS; now it is the IAS] who are a rigid caste by themselves like Brahmins. Nobody with even greater and authoritative knowledge can be smuggled into their sphere ... He [the ICS officer] can be anything — a district magistrate, a director of industries, a district judge, a trade commissioner, a financial adviser or even war controller of Persian Gulf. This system makes him a jack of all trades but master of none. It is natural, therefore, that when he is put in charge of several controls, say food, cloth, transport, etc., there is an utter confusion not due to the lack of interest but on account of lack of knowledge ... The result is chaos ...

Saha also quotes Sir Michael Sadler who writes:

> Administrative officials seem weak in the field of imaginative and

creative suggestion — in the points which characterize original minds. If you read an official file, you will find as a rule that the experienced official is better at telling a subordinate what *NOT* to do than at interesting him in ways of doing better ...

It has often been suggested that the remedy is to appoint scientists to high administrative posts. To be fair, the Government has occasionally done this but alas, often the remedy has proved worse than the disease! There are of course many reasons but let us hear what Saha said way back in 1937 while addressing the Indian Physical Society.

It has been our sad experience that when a Government Department takes upon itself the task of carrying on fundamental research work [Saha is here referring to research carried on in A.I.R.], the duties of the officer engaged for the purpose very often begin and end in going through interminable series of official files and the officer is hardly allowed any time for quiet thinking and sustained work; the desire of the Government to carry out such investigations ultimately reduces to mere pious hope.

Strangely, it seems as if nobody is able to do anything about this virus. Listen to what Nehru had to say on the subject of bureaucracy. Speaking at a Science Congress he once said:

When we started it [the present Planning Commission], I thought it should not function as a part of the Government. But now it is like any other part of Government ... the same hierarchy of Secretaries, Under-Secretaries and what not — it is frightening. What was thought of as a close body of people who think and advise Government has now grown into a huge organisation with all the Departments of Government duplicated there, and each one sending papers to the other which is the normal habit of Government.

Nehru was concerned that the scientific establishments were faring no better (as Saha had earlier declared). He said:

I had hoped that science at least would escape that numbing influence of the Governmental way of working. I do not know how far we have succeeded. I rather doubt it. I am inclined to think some of our laboratories are gradually succumbing to the Governmental way.

Is there any faint ray of hope? None that I can see. Enough on this depressing subject!

9.5.5 Saha on our archaic taxation system

Turning to something different, I wonder how many of you have followed from the newspapers the agitation to remove an obnoxious levy called octroi. On this subject, as early as 1953, Saha wrote:

> Soviet Russia also had a perplexing number of local sales tax, octrois etc. ... before the introduction of the turn-over tax. The introduction of this tax in place of a plethora of annoying taxes made it possible for Soviet Russia to plough back a major part of the Nation's earnings to profitable investment ...
>
> The taxation system of this country is not only complex, but is such that it is capable of evasion a..d tax is not easily realisable. It ought to be radically simplified, so that maximum amount possible of the Nation's earnings can be ploughed back to investment.

Many have actually tried simplification, including one Prime Minister. But the bureaucracy has successfully resisted changes. I leave you to guess the reason! The irony is that recently a Committee of Chief Ministers was appointed to review the case for octroi. The Chairman of the Committee is a Marxist and he was most vocal in *support* of octroi! I wonder what Saha would have said about that!!

9.6 Entry into politics

It was inevitable that Saha would eventually land in politics. Immediately after Independence, elections were held to the Constituent Assembly (whose job it was to draft a Constitution). Sharat Chandra Bose, the brother of Netaji, asked Saha to stand as a Congress candidate from Calcutta and Saha agreed. At this stage a senior Congressman called on Saha and their conversation went as follows:

Visitor: Why have you got your name proposed for election to the Constituent Assembly?

Saha: I did so at the request of Sharat Chandra Bose who thought my advice on national planning, industrialisation and river valley planning would be very helpful ...

Visitor: Do you know your nomination cannot be accepted?

Saha: Why?

Visitor: Because you have persistently spoken against charka and khaddar which would be the cardinal points of Congress activity. Are you willing to recant?

Saha: Decidedly no.

Visitor: Why?

Saha: Because I believe and have proved this insistence on primitive technology shows a retrograde and anti-scientific mentality, and persons who are wedded to this mentality would bring disaster to the country when they are in power.

Visitor: If this is your opinion, you cannot get the nomination.

Saha: If this is your condition, I am not keen ... for I hold science dearer than your slogans.

After the Constitution was framed and adopted, elections were held for the first time in 1951 in the new republic and this time Saha offered himself as an Independent candidate from N.W. Calcutta constituency. He won by a large margin defeating his nearest Congress rival and at last he could challenge the Government on the floor of the House. He took every opportunity to pull the Government up, especially on matters relating to planning and development. By now Katju was at the Centre, serving as the Home Minister. The old animosity surfaced and Katju patronisingly advised Saha to confine himself to the laboratory; Saha gave a fitting reply.

9.7 The end

In early 1956, Saha developed serious health problems on account of high blood pressure. His doctors advised him to slow down. He merely smiled and continued as ever. On February 14, he had an appointment with his old friend Mahalanobis, now a favourite of Nehru and closely associated with the planning process. Saha went walking towards the Planning Commission Office but enroute he collapsed. He was recognised and rushed to a hospital but did not recover; he had passed into history.

As we have seen, in later years Saha was critical of many things. Commenting on this aspect, D.M. Bose has observed:

> In a democratic set up it is necessary that some of the able men, who have a first-hand knowledge of such problems should be able to criticise all important proposals for national reconstruction.

In other words, Saha played the role of a conscience keeper. No doubt he functioned in the Opposition in Parliament but did so observing the dignity and decorum of the House (unlike what one often witnesses these days). Saha was smart and he could achieve with sarcasm and cutting logic what is now sought to be done with shouting and walkouts.

Although he functioned in the Opposition, in his heart of hearts he does not seem to have relished his role. When Dr. Radhakrishnan was elected Vice President, Saha in a congratulatory letter sent to him wrote:

Fate has ordained that I shall be in opposition but I hope my friendship with Panditji will stand the strain. I am reminded of a Puranic story where Jayan and Vijayan, attendants of Vishnu, were cursed by an angry sage to undergo the pangs of birth, but were told that if they preferred to be born as enemies of Vishnu, they would be freed from the curse after three births, but if born as devotees, it would require seven births. So naturally they preferred to be born as enemies. I have the same consolation.

It was said of him (Saha):

He was extremely simple, almost austere in habits and personal needs. Outwardly he sometimes gave the impression of being remote, matter of fact, even harsh ... It was not in his nature to placate others.

Today, the extreme socialist model that Saha strongly advocated stands discredited and has been abandoned all over Eastern Europe where it once was religiously practised by Communist Governments. At the other end, quite apart from the type of ism involved, mankind has come to realise that uncontrolled industrial growth is not exactly a blessing. On the one hand it has led to unnecessary and undesirable pollution of the environment. On the other hand it has created a mania for consumerism, bringing in its wake its own package of social evils. Seen in this context, Gandhism, if one might call it that, is neither stupid nor retrograde. It is a sane prescription for life which has much to commend.

Whether we can all become Mahatmas is a different question (Saha often said, "We can have only one Mahatma!") but Gandhism definitely does not stand discredited. Does it mean that Saha was wrong in opposing Gandhi's views on development? May be so from a historical point but that should not cloud our judgement.

Two things we must bear in mind. The first is — and this is *most* important — Saha, as much as Gandhi (and for that matter Nehru too), wanted "every tear wiped from every eye"; only, his perception of how to do it was different. Secondly, Gandhism not withstanding, in this world we *do* need a certain amount of industrialisation. To give an example, Gandhi did not walk from place to place (as the late Paramacharya of Kanchi did within living memory); instead he travelled by train; he had a pocket watch; he used loud speakers at prayer meetings; and so on. In short, Gandhi *did* depend on modern technology. What Gandhism really means therefore is that technology should not dominate our minds; rather there should be a balanced blend with ancient values.

Enough of this philosophical digression! Where Saha is concerned, there is no need to pass judgement about whether he was right or wrong in his predictions. We have the advantage of hind sight whereas he did not. What is relevant are his basic feelings. Whatever he did or said on the national scene sprang from a passionate love for his countrymen and a deep desire that they should be free from poverty, hunger, disease and illiteracy. That is all that matters, and can anyone take objection to that?

9.8 Looking back

And so we come to the end of this volume. We have seen Saha from many sides, especially as an enquiring scientist at one end and as a public-spirited citizen at the other, keen to exploit the fruits of science to fight disease, hunger, poverty, illiteracy, etc.

The pure scientist is often lost in the beauty and grandeur of Nature as revealed to him in his discoveries, and he is therefore all the time in pursuit of new discoveries. In this sense he is rather like a painter or a musician, and in fact Raman once described science as the highest form of creative art. On the other hand, science is different from art in that it generates knowledge and as Confucius put it, "the essence of knowledge is that having it one must use it." Saha's point was: Who else but a scientist can show how the knowledge generated by him can be put to use?

Thanks to fairly generous funding, there is today no dearth of competent and even good scientists — we have a reasonable number of them. But what is in short supply is the *selfless public spirit and the commitment to the Nation* that Saha exhibited in such abundant measure. For that reason, compared to Indian scientists of today, *Saha stands mighty tall.*

Present-day scientists have their own excuses for staying away from matters of national concern. Some of their arguments for doing so may be justifiable, but many others are not. Take a simple example like teaching. Only a small fraction of our active and bright research physicists do any teaching and hardly any one among them is doing anything to help our college teachers or to improve the standards of teaching. They all want public funds for research, travel, etc., but thereafter everyone shuts the public out of his or her mind and withdraws into the ivory tower.

Physics is the mother of all technologies. It was so in the last century and it has remained so to this day. In other countries the importance of physics to society is widely recognized and accepted, but in this country it hardly is, inspite of the advantages we inherited from people like Raman, Bose, Saha and Bhabha. For this, only our present-day physicists are to blame.

Consider laser technology for instance. The first laser in India was built within three or four years after the first laser was demonstrated in America. Yet, quarter of a century later, we can't buy a simple, milliwatt power, Helium–Neon laser of Indian make — we have to *import* it. A lot of money has been pumped into laser research in the country and we do hear a lot about powerful lasers built in various labs, but the simple fact is that if we want an ordinary laser to teach optics in colleges, we have to import it. Why? Is it so in Russia and China? Then why only in India is it different? Few are bothered by such questions — and this sample is not even the tip of the iceberg. No wonder, our industrialists for example care two hoots for our physicists.

Next take national concern. When Russia launched the first-ever satellite (Sputnik I) in 1958, it sent shock waves all across America. The Americans simply couldn't believe that someone else could get ahead of them! The Sputnik shock galvanised the whole country as it were, every sector of it. And in the revamping that occurred, scientists played a prominent part. Contrast this with our situation. Some time ago, America applied strong pressure on Russia not to supply know-how for cryoengines to this country; it went further and tried to block even the sale of readymade engines. The newspapers were full of these strong-arm tactics of America, but none of our scientific bodies spoke up or expressed solidarity with our space organisation. Would Saha have remained silent had he been alive?

It is well known that the scientists of tomorrow are moulded in the schools of today. Look at the educational sector in the country. It is lying in shambles thanks to corrupt and misguided forces (largely political). And yet, no one is protesting. Like the venerable Bhishma in the Mahabharata, our intellectuals (scientists especially) are choosing to remain silent spectators despite the gravity of the situation. This is in marked contrast to the protective instincts of other groups – let the Government try to interfere with the Press and see what journalists do; let the Government try to pass a rule that affects the film industry and see what actors and film workers do. I am not suggesting that scientists also should take to the streets — Saha never did that. But like a concerned person he spoke out repeatedly and also wrote with passion;that is what is missing today.

Some may feel I am being emotive and am exaggerating. Well, I leave you to see, absorb, reflect and decide. Meanwhile let me, by way of substantiating my views, refer to a letter I received a couple of years ago from a young science teacher in Bengal. I don't know this person, have never met him and am not likely to either. I don't know how he knew my name and got hold of my address. Anyway, this is what he wrote (in part):

> My purpose of writing is to draw your kind attention to how we, *the villagers are receding from the benefits of science and technology day by day*. There is a gap between vision and reality even after 45 years of independence. Does science and technology benefit the rural people? Does it provide sufficient help to them? ...
>
> I am a science teacher living in a village in a very interior part of the country ... Generally speaking, we do not know how much our country has progressed or how our reputed scientists are working ...

This letter came from Bengal, the home of Saha!
In 1935 Saha wrote:

> In poverty, ignorance and disease, India of today can only be classed with China and Abyssinia [Ethiopia], countries which are still steeped in medievalism ...

Sixty years later, China is a major world power having conquered poverty, illiteracy and disease. What about India? True we are now far ahead of Ethiopia but we have a long long way to go to catch up with China; somewhere somehow we seem to have missed the boat.

If things are in a bad mess today, it is due to the evaporation of idealism in the post-Independence generations; and here I am willing to carry my share of the blame!

Nearly two centuries ago the English poet Wordsworth wrote of the great John Milton:

> Milton! thou shouldst be living at this hour:
> England hath need of thee ..
> ... We are selfish men;
> Oh! raise us up, return to us again;
> And give us manners, virtue, freedom, power.
> Thy soul was like a Star, and dwelt apart;
> Thou hadst a voice whose sound was like the sea: ...

We could say likewise of Saha; we need him again. Alas, the dead don't come back but their spirit can return. Dear young reader, why don't you, when you grow up, don the mantle that Saha once wore? The country is waiting ...

Box 9.2 The following are some of the tributes paid to Saha on the occasion of his sixtieth birthday in 1953.

A.H. Compton (Nobel Laureate)

It is a pleasure to have the opportunity of congratulating you on the occasion of your sixtieth birthday for your outstanding achievements, especially in the field of thermodynamics. As you may know, I at one time had the honour of nominating you for the Nobel Prize for your work in this area ...

Enrico Fermi (Nobel Laureate)

I still remember with great pleasure the inspiration that I received from reading Professor Meghnad Saha's fundamental contributions to the theory of gas ionisation ...

E.O. Lawrence (Nobel Laureate)

I have known and admired him for many years. Indeed, I shall never forget the intellectual thrill I derived from learning about "Saha's ionisation equation" in my early days as a graduate student ...

Harlow Shapley, Harvard Observatory

The Harvard Observatory owes much to Professor Meghnad Saha. His pioneer work thirty years ago on temperature ionisations in sun and stars inspired the activities of British scientists who in turn inspired the work here at Harvard of Mrs. Cecilia Payne-Gaposchkin, Donald M. Menzel and Frank Hogg; and their work established modern astrophysics in Harvard ...

Harold Urey (Nobel Laureate)

Many years ago when I was a graduate student at California, I was working on some things in connection with the ionisation of the alkali metals — a problem which I never succeeded in finishing. In the course of this work I read with great interest your [Saha's] very important publication of that time on the ionisation as it affected the spectra of the star. It was in fact one of the first scientific papers which I read with very great care as a graduate student ... I greatly admired this publication and it has been referred to over and over again in the years since ...

Donald H. Menzel, Harvard Observatory

His [Saha's] early contributions to astrophysics were my first inspiration in the subject. The famous theorem that bears his name has been the key that has unlocked the secret of stellar atmospheres ...

James Frank

I remember vividly the time when your great contribution ... was first published and the great impression it immediately made ... Still we could not foresee at that time that this paper was destined to open up an entirely new chapter in modern astrophysics — the importance of which cannot be over estimated ...

Walter Adams (earlier at Mount Wilson)

Among the many contributions of Professor Saha to the field of astrophysics, I should rank most highly his brilliant discoveries in the theory of ionisation and its application to the spectra of the sun and stars. These investigations have provided a new and rational explanation for many of the observed phenomena in astronomy and have opened a broad and fruitful field of research. Every scientist owes Professor Saha a deep debt of gratitude ...

A.V. Hill, F.R.S.

Greetings to Meghnad Saha on his sixtieth birthday: may he have many years of fruitful scientific activity ahead of him! After all, what is sixty? Pavlov invented the subject of Conditioned Reflexes when he was 55 and had not finished working on it when he was 86. His friends expect no less from Meghnad Saha, and wish him all joy in it.

J.B.S. Haldane, F.R.S.

May I also be allowed to congratulate him on his recent successful re-entry into politics? India (and Britain too) needs men who will bring some understanding of science to the government of the country.

Max Born (Nobel Laureate)

I vividly remember the immense impression produced by his first and celebrated work on the intensities of absorption lines in stellar spectra as explained in terms of the statistical equilibrium of different states of ionisation ...

Spencer Jones, F.R.S. (Astronomer Royal)

I well remember how, on the publication of his early and important paper on ionisation in stellar atmosphere, the late Professor Alfred Fowler drew my attention to it and emphasized its fundamental importance. And so it proved, for this paper was the stimulus to the work of Milne, R.H. Fowler, and others in subsequent years. In fact, almost all work on stellar atmosphere has been based on it, either directly or indirectly. The paper provided a new method of attack and opened the way to the solution of many problems that had been puzzling.

Index

Note: Page numbers in brackets refer to illustrations